12 Tribes Rising

From Eternity's Fire

by Alexandria

ISBN: 978-0-615-43382-0
Library of Congress Cataloging-in-Publication Data available upon
request.

This book is printed on acid-free paper and meets all ANSI
standards for archival quality.

Dedicated to

Grama-Far-Away for making sure I knew it was real.
Grama-Across-the-Street for a childhood filled with love.
My Guides for their patience, support and guardianship.
And Mitchell, for cheering me on to the finish line.

Table of Contents

Prologue

"Oh, this place is *definitely* haunted," declared the taxi driver who had just spent the entirety of the journey from London-Heathrow airport providing me with a multitude of historical facts as the countryside passed us by. But the interstate looked more like Virginia, with little to see, so he had digressed into the personal details of his life to pass the hour and a half ride to Stansted Hall. He had declared himself an Atheist-married-to-a-Muslim, among other things, and his endless chatter in the British accent was amusing. I had slept only a couple of hours on the transcontinental flight, and now, as the first glimpse of Stansted Hall came into view, I felt an edge of panic at my choice to come.

But I am no stranger to jumping off cliffs in life, though I do believe it is a tendency whose accuracy may be improved upon as my centeredness and connection to spirit and higher self improves. And it's that quest that now brought me to stand on the front steps of this place on the other side of the world.

I had carefully kept my own side of the conversation with the driver away from the actual details of the week-long training I was about to undertake. Arthur Findlay College had conveniently called it an "International week." I simply told anyone who asked that I was attending an international conference. If they pushed me further, (and interestingly, most did not) to inquire about the actual topic, I said it was training for counselors. This was honest and made perfect sense, since I had spent the last three years providing a range of counseling services to clients in the midst of my business consulting.

Now however, that inevitable moment struck me, as it often does when I arrive at the destination of a decision, and I heard myself mutter *"Oh, God…what have I done. Have I lost my mind…?! What am I doing here..?!"* A second prayer followed mentally, as I wished for nice accommodations at the very least.

Somewhere between turning down the driveway, and stepping out of the van, it was starting to dawn on my very opinionated driver, that perhaps his passenger had not shared (in its entirety) the purpose of her trip.

"*Hey…..*" he said rather slowly as he read the metal sign at the gate and got his first view of the mansion and estate. "I've heard of this place….I think….what did you say you were coming here to study..?" he asked a bit suspiciously.

Nearing the end of my rope as I wrestled with my own rising panic, jet lag and feeling ever-so-close to a possible moment in my life where I might be surrounded by acceptance, I turned to the man with one of my personalities I refer to as the-girl-that-doesn't-take-any-shit' and pierced him with a look.

"Do you really want to know?" I replied, with a warning in my tone that announced that he was going to get the truth whether it made him comfortable of not.

"Yeah…" he answered, though with a bit of hesitation.

"Mediumship," I stated simply.

His next pause didn't last long, as I knew it wouldn't, and he began explaining another branch of his family that included a witch. I brushed over his conversation from there, assuring him this had nothing to do with witches, and became lost in my own thoughts as he continued to banter all the way up to the huge entry door carrying my bag. From there, a sort of reverence, or perhaps fear quieted him. And beyond a brief sales-pitch to the front desk attendant, he was gone.

For my part, relief dawned in gradual steps from the friendly receptionist I had spent time with by telephone to book my reservations, to the discovery that the estate was absolutely beautiful, and my accommodations excellent in their simplicity. I had arrived at a safe and welcoming destination, whatever the rest of the week might bring.

A Glimpse at the Underground Work

It seems an important thing to begin at the beginning. Though my week at Stansted Hall, Arthur Findlay College provided the launching point in understanding the core purpose of my life, it was certainly not the true starting point of the journey. How can the immensity of the "turning on" of my metaphysical abilities ever be truly appreciated if the elements and experiences of the first 33 years of this life are skipped over? I have always been a "sensitive," but experienced it only as clairsentient discomfort, with no formal instruction or explanations. It's important to understand that I was pushed through a mostly "normal" life of family-school-corporate career until that week in September 2003 that changed it all. And though my book-learning regarding metaphysical subjects started years prior to this; my true abilities were not fully revealed to me until that training in England.

I studied for nearly eleven years in metaphysics prior to arriving in the United Kingdom, and during that time one of the projects I embarked upon was to create a journal of-sorts, with pictures to guide me. It started at birth and covered every important relationship and subject of my life. My first teacher started the assignment and called it "doing the underground work." It was a journey into self-realization that few have the courage for because it requires such naked honesty. But deep healing can be the result, and I would recommend this kind of exercise to everyone.

So in the interests of full disclosure and to help you see how all of the puzzle pieces fit together, a few of the core excerpts are inserted and shared here at the beginning. I believe that this will help you to understand the child, the girl and the woman I am… and the person who went to study in England. Perhaps in my life experiences, trials and metaphysical awakenings, you may find a mirror in some of your own. This journey and story will then take you out into the world and provide a Practitioner's Guide that you can personally use and implement. This is both an amazing and difficult time in human history, and this guide can help you expand, manage and understand your own sensitivities.

I hope you can also understand that it is not without personal discomfort that I share the traumas and joys of my life. Some of the choices and occurrences revealed in these pages I have never discussed with anyone. But, I often thought as I would hesitate in my writing, perhaps that's the point. The life and the story are made up of *all* of these parts. If I hold back a piece out of vanity or fear, then I am not truly assisting others who may be struggling with the exact same issues.

In an effort to honor those I have walked with in this lifetime, their names have been changed in this book to assure their privacy. I am especially sensitive to the awareness that this revealing will be painful to my parents should they ever encounter it, but I share this with love in my heart for them and all who struggle, that perhaps the miracles and magic I now know, they might accept one day.

Reaching for healing is a choice.

The Early Years

The Early Years

Entering a Life

I was born in upstate New York on a July day in 1970 into the arms of a truly caring woman. She had graduated from nursing school, and was officially a healer to the world. Some people are just born mothers. I might choose to be, one day. But I feel more that my purpose in this life is teacher, example, warrior and leader. Though these each are done with the intent to heal. I believe that I selected her in part because after many traumatic lifetimes, I needed a lioness that would dedicate herself to helping me feel safe and loved in the early years, in a life destined for much awakening and completion.

My mother, I was not to learn until later, also carried and taught me great fear of the world and everything in it; as she was taught by her parents before her. She also harbored a deep, and very subconscious jealousy and meanness toward me that was a carry over from a past lifetime. There is no denying that she loved me, but later in life her own unhappiness would turn a great deal of her behavior toward me rancid in the undercurrent of it, both mentally and emotionally.

Some things I know for certain from my early childhood. I had a deep connection to nature and animals. I was loved. I was wanted. I was safe. And up to the age of about fourteen I never "wanted" for anything. I am told my parents didn't have much money, and that my needs always came before their own. Sacrifice of this nature is always a double-edged sword. Though the parents give themselves away in the name of love, it also carries a price to be exacted when the child comes of age. War stories of sacrifice demand guilt and return on their "investment." The belief system handed me said that you have children and give up your life so that when you're old they will take care of you. Though I know love is present, I also believe that much of it was laced with unspoken conditions to be exacted later. Guilt, obligation and fear…what a horrible legacy. I made the decision that should I ever choose to have children of my own, I would do so without these conditions being put on love. I bless my parents for their courage in the face of inheriting such a legacy themselves.

I have had more than one discussion with my mother about the concept of "family." In truth, I think being an old soul with great depths of sensitivity brought my awareness to levels my parents could never understand. In many ways, I was the adult in the house by age four, and more than a little bit psychic and mediumistic. My mother jokes about several elements from the early days starting with the fact that my father would come home from work late and find me standing in the crib. I always knew when he was arriving before the door even opened. My bedroom would be dark, and I would say *Daddy, there's a man standing in the corner.* It scared the daylights out of him. Retelling that story now, I'm certain I was seeing my guides. And a beautiful, sensitive child I was, who knew that these earth "parents" were somehow not her *true* family. But as I grew up through the early days, I can remember shifting out of fear and to try to please them. Mediumship was greatly shut down or relegated to a creative imagination when I was told I was incorrect. And fear creped in to claim clairvoyant clear sight. I can vividly remember the moment I no longer allowed my third eye to see when my eyes were closed. I was watching something scary on television and declared that I wanted the ability to "see" with my physical eyes *closed* to stop.

These facts and what was yet to come do not change my love for them, but much of the truth of it is a discussion I could never have. The closest my mother and I came to an explanation angered her greatly. I said that the definition of family, are those who honor your choices and treat you with kindness. She demanded that blood relations are family no matter what.

I knew better. I remembered home.

When I Was Four, We had a Baby

Well, actually, *I* had a baby. Though I'm certain my mother would disagree with that conclusion. My brother and childhood companion had arrived. He was born in 1974. A true light in my life. The sparkle of this little Gemini child was always sunshine amid a house full of Cancer emotions. We were constant companions for nearly ten years, at play, on vacations, etc. He was tiny and quite sickly in his first few years. I thank God for this great friendship in my life. I'm glad the two of us choose such a large part of the adventure to be together. Of those earliest years I remember many toys, much play time, beautiful holidays, fall leaves and white Christmases.

I had an incredibly nice childhood…at home. Pets, country landscapes, butterflies, flowers, breathtaking autumn foliage, tons of toys, the sandbox, swings, forts, climbing trees in the woods, holidays, family excursions, the pumpkin farm, riding bikes…..and Grama-across-the-street.

That was what we called her. Our full-time babysitter and loving friend who practically raised us. Another fact my mother would take great exception to, but Grama and Brother were truly my childhood companions in this life, since both of my parents worked long hours. I loved her house, her cooking….applesauce, cakes, cookies, salads shaped like raggedy-ann dolls. The ultimate Grama she was. I can see now as I look back that I was taught subconsciously that *food was love*. Cooking was an event, eating was an event, holidays are some of my favorite memories, and they were always about the food. Even at regular meals I was told how wonderful I was that I ate such a good quantity like my Dad. I was trained from an early age that food was joy and approval, and emotional eating was a dilemma that I would struggle with in later years as a result.

Out Into The World

When I first saw a picture of myself standing at the school bus stop for kindergarten, the fact that I was incredibly cute was quickly overtaken by a gripping sorrow and vulnerable fear in my solar plexus and head. I wanted to run into the picture, gather the tiny child in my arms and protect her from the months and years ahead. You see, school days meant leaving the protection of mother, home and Grama…and I was so small and so afraid of *everything*. A fact which I now know had everything to do with being a "sensitive" and "empath." I felt everything and everyone clairsentiently and it was tremendously uncomfortable with no explanation or way of knowing what the actual problem was…beyond the standard school yard and human issue explanations.

The neighborhood I grew up in set the stage for my interactions with people, and was comprised of households with children at three age group levels. The "big brothers" who were two years older than us girls, and the "little brothers" about 2-4 years younger. The other piece of the neighborhood hierarchy to know is that all of the fathers worked for the same large corporation, and the wives were all housewives.

So what does this have to do with anything?

I was the only girl without a big brother, my father the only one who worked for a competing corporation, and my mom worked full time and wasn't part of the "housewife click." And so the merciless teasing and tormenting began…. at about age 6. It was horrible. How can children be so cruel? All of the girls had older brothers, but I had no protection. They ripped me apart emotionally and verbally…and sometimes it even got physical. This went on for years and years. I still sometimes have nightmares about riding on the school bus. I was about seven years old when I started diving into my imagination for companionship and protection, and looking for a hero in the world who might protect me. My relationship with television and movies started here.

<u>My First Hero</u>

I find it interesting to see how we as children are "imprinted" like puppies by experiences; and then carry that memory around even if we don't realize where it came from.

When I was about 6 years old my mother tirelessly signed me up and took me to summer swimming lessons at the indoor High School pool. For weeks and weeks I refused to get in the water, and when I did, I clung to the side of the pool for dear life. In addition to the discomfort that can come from psychic abilities being amplified by water, I am very certain I drown in a past lifetime. This helps explain my terror of the water. And having gotten nowhere that summer with the first two attempts, she signed me up for a third week of classes.

His name was Pat, and it was love at first sight for both of us. My desire to be in his arms was stronger that my fear. I couldn't wait for it to be "my turn." I can still close my eyes and see him. Dark short hair, big hands, strong arms, broad shoulders. He used to find ways to pass four to eight other children off to other instructors, so he could play and swim only with me. He would put me on his back and take me into the deep end of the pool. I even jumped off the high diving board to him. He always caught me. I was brave for him. I realized in adulthood that I find his physical features to be the sexiest thing in the world. A fact that never ceases to amuse me.

Drama & My Father

Mostly what I remember of my father in my early years is that he provided a beautiful home, spectacular holidays, and worked very hard. When I close my eyes and "feel" him during my childhood, I get a sense of emotional "distance" due to his never being taught by his own father how to express affection. I feel his depression and disappointment at not being "satisfied" with his work and life.

As all little girls seek the approval of their fathers, I too, set out to get his attention. My mother was tireless in her dedication to ballet lessons, girl scouts, organ lessons, and so much more. But it was rare that my father was in attendance, and when he was, the moody undertone of anger always appeared about it sooner or later. And mom spent her whole life making excuses for him. I understand now that it was emotional and verbal abuse from the ungrounded anger that raged within him. His abuse wasn't physical; quite the contrary. He used silence and the removal of his love as punishment. Between that and my mother's drama, it would seem that I learned that dramatics got the attention I desired. Add that to my increasing imagination and the television storylines that fed and nourished my sense of aloneness, and it's easy to see how the little girl came to unconsciously believe that attention and love from men where to be found by drama. It was shocking for me to find that the actual physical touch of a man, even holding my hand, was an astounding and foreign sensation. I was ashamed that I craved it and yet felt I must be unworthy of it to have had it withheld for so long... even from my father.

Suffer the Little Children

A little boy and girl sat huddled together on the darkened stairs. We were certain someone would hear us, though our soft, footed pajamas made no sound on the gold carpet of the stairs, as we crept down from our rooms. They though we were in bed. And we had been. I guess I was about eight years old, and my Brother four. His bedroom was closest to the stairs, so when he heard it, he had come to get me. His eyes wide with fear, his tiny hands touching my face. We hardly dared to breathe as we sat together in the dark outside the downstairs den and listened... listened in horror at Dad screaming at Mom.

He was ranting and slamming things. Mom was sobbing. I don't remember the exact details of the fight, only that he seemed irrational and out-of-control. I knew he was "abusing" her, though not physically. I remember her sobbing,

"What do you want from me?!?
What do you want me to do?!?

I also remembered thinking our family was over. There was to be an uncomfortable knowingness in both my brother and I from that day forward that all was not well, and that the storms would come again. Little did I know that by the time I was fifteen,

12 Tribes Rising from Eternity's Fire   Page 17

it would be me on the receiving end of Dad's wrath. My father taught me helpless despair that night.

Looking Back on the School Years

When I came across my senior high school photo from 1988, I was taken back by how beautiful I found myself to be. I have always referred to high school as a "graceless age," and yet, somehow, though the memories of emotional obsessions, braces, pimples and being "too fat" are not forgotten, that was not what struck me as I looked at this picture. Instead, I saw an exotically beautiful girl with stunning eyes, soft curls, and a perfect face. Even with the braces I should not have had a reason to feel such constant shame over my appearance.

Today it occurs to me that self-loathing is two-fold. Yes, it's true that the media taught me I wasn't good enough, and my aunt had callously confirmed it one day that I would never be pretty in comparison to my beauty queen cousin; but it was ME who believed it and continued the hideous betrayal of my authentic self for years to come. Looking at that photo later, I am certain they were not correct.

Religion & Faith

We marched in the snow and ice to the Catholic "church school" as we called it, every Wednesday afternoon. We ranged in age from 6-8. Silence or false smiles were the keys to the gate where Sister Ann stood. She was the most horrible disciplinarian to walk the earth, and if you were unfortunate enough to have her as a substitute teacher that day, even God couldn't help you if you weren't "perfect."

Even to a child of seven it made no sense. There was no love or upliftment to the system being shoved down our throats. And to make it more personally difficult, Mom (the devout Catholic), and Dad (the angry atheist), fought constantly about whether attendance at Sunday services and putting the children in "church school" was appropriate at all.

For me, the most memorable occurrence was an assembly in the basement of the church rectory one cold afternoon. We were marched in silence to sit before the almighty Father H. who was gracing us with his presence, which was rare. But it was not wisdom or love he gave to the small children; it was anger and fear. I may have been young, but I was "older" than this man of 50 years in my knowingness that you do NOT tell seven year old children they are sinners who will burn in hell. You tell them they are hope and light and sunshine. You tell them that they are beautiful and talented and loved. I was done with the "church" at age seven. And our judgmental, hypocritical neighbors assisted me in making that decision. One afternoon, one of the neighborhood mothers made me help her daughter set the dining room table for a dinner in honor of Father H. All the parents were invited except for mine…because we did not attend Sunday mass *every* weekend as good Catholics should.

I'm not sure I had anything that resembled faith based on the education I received. I actually had not been taught anything of God except that if you begged enough he sent an occasional miracle to earth, but only if he was in the mood. The saying "Sometimes bad things happen to good people" echoed in me for so many years and had far-reaching ramifications. Between my fear and psychic oversensitivity, even as late as my freshman year in college I used to run to my car between classes and for lunch, because I was terrified to even *sit* in a building around the other students outside of class.

I think the majority of my faith was placed in the unswerving protection of my parents no matter the crisis, and maybe in the fact that if I worked VERY hard, through the educational process I might achieve something. But mostly, I just begged God for things in tears, though I was sure his convenience was not always with me, and I was angry that he allowed and played games through our suffering.

Hiding in my Room

No wonder I hid. God in general didn't seem to care. The "system" demanded an unachievable perfection. The world was a terrible, random, frightening place. And by the time I turned sixteen, my fathers' irrational wrath replaced any notions I had of being protected as his "little girl." I know now that a large part of the discomfort I felt *everywhere*, was because I instantly "knew" things. I think life would have been SO different if I had been provided with even the slightest bit of education about my abilities. I could feel disapproval and negative thoughts and energy instantly from people. I experienced telepathy via feeling and knowingness rather than hearing sentences. The energy of places, emotions, thoughts and even people's intentions would just hit me like a brick. And naturally, my human parents labeled me with irritation as simply being "too sensitive." A label used constantly to explain their ongoing array of disapproval whenever I tried to resist doing what they wanted.

It was a tough road and in high school, after my father came home from work in the evenings, the scenario was always the same. If you kissed up to him he didn't verbally rip you in half…until he had "a drink." Then, in the middle of dinner like clock work the explosion came. Irrational, ungrounded, and seething with anger. He would declare me a loser on a regular basis, though I was a straight-A student who had no issues with drugs, boyfriends or bad choices. And I would retreat to my room to eat and hide. And the characters on television became my family. What else did I have? Where could I go? I always thanked God for my incredible imagination and clarity of creating other worlds in my mind. People to love me, places to hide, companions to protect me.

So I created and spent time with the family I created in my head, and together we traveled to some of the most amazing places. I would not learn until later that my 'abilities' actually did allow me to journey to other places, and that not all of the characters were 'imaginary', as my guides would pick up the energy of a "character" and step in regularly to provide support. I longed to travel the world and see the beauty I knew that nature and history provided. I collected hundreds of pictures and brochures, and saved for three years to afford my first trip to a ranch in the rocky mountains of Colorado. Beyond it all, I believed in the magnificence of what a life could be meant for.

Stepping Out of the Matrix

At age 28, I was told by a life counselor that I needed to stop living in my head so much, and the shock of finding myself standing on the physical plane in the center of my life was overwhelming. I thought I was going to die as the world came into focus and I found myself standing "alone" despite having a busy career, friends and human family. I realized at once that I couldn't remember the last time I'd actually been "here" fully. I know this will seem a strange concept… to no one more than myself at the time. But at some point maybe age 8 or 9, I found this "other" plane of existence… of a reality in my mind that was a playground and total retreat. In this place I could hide, have anything I desired, go to far off places, and be with people I choose, loved and trusted. At some point this other plane of existence had become my home… my family. As I walked through daily life, I was here only as little as was necessary to exist; then I would run back into my "fantasies" to escape a world that seemed to be without happy endings, without comfort, without protection, without nourishment. And when life threw a crisis at me, I would bring the "protectors" and "family" into the physical with my imagination…to literally stand between me and the abuser. Television had brought to me the characters of my "family." I played with them, rode horses with them, ran with them…and they never let me down. Never hurt me. For years, as I excelled in school and a business career, not a living soul would ever have guessed I was living two lives. (And at the time, I had no idea how real those other family members were.) To the world, I presented as a totally appropriate professional.

By age 28 the "other reality" was so complete, so automatic in its presence every minute, that my conscious decision to try to leave it behind as if it was inappropriate, was *beyond* a shock to my system. It was a fact that I had never been without a "fictitious" companion in the room. I felt bereft and alone with no education to know that many of those companions were my spirit guides. In an effort to be more appropriate, I tried to follow human psychology. Determined to try to stop retreating from the world and use that energy to expand into the "real" world instead. I felt something akin to grief. And now I know that without the understanding of who and what I was, this psychology exercise was a bit incorrect for me.

In Search of My Life

At the risk of sounding way too cliché, the search for my life has led me down many winding roads. A root belief in my self was always overshadowed by low self-esteem. I attracted to me controlling women in career positions and friendships that always ended dramatically and sadly. I gave my talents to groups without realizing I was hoping to help them to have *their* dreams, so that they would someday "take care of me". After ruptured ovarian cysts and surgery at age 19, my weight took ten years to balloon at 174 pounds, and though I was still hoping to find a wonderful man to marry, I had barely even dated up to age 29.

On Thanksgiving Day 1999, I found myself sitting alone on the most beautiful beach I had ever seen in Navarre, Florida. My parents and I had driven the 12-hour trek to visit my brother for the holiday. I would have to say it was one of the worst family gatherings I have ever suffered through.

And I ran.

My family ostracized me with unbearable emotional cruelty, and though I can't remember the exact circumstances, I have never felt so hurt or alone or without "true family." So I ran to the white sand beach of Navarre. It was breathtaking in its beauty of white sand, privacy and pink sunset. Like being transported to another planet and comforted and loved by magic itself. Not even in my fantasies had I seen anything that could compare.

I can look back now and recognize that my Guides and nature spirits had manifested it with such love for me. Crabs played at my feet, and wild dolphins broke the surface of the blue, clear waters. Sting rays glided by, as the most astounding pink and purple sunset was painted across the sky, and a full moon rose. This experience brought me to the decision to take control. On November 29, 1999 I walked into a medical weight loss clinic at 174 pounds; and by April 2000 I had achieved a weight loss of 40 pounds.

This was age 29.

I would take my first lover that year. Definitely not a magical experience. But a necessary one. I needed to experience my sexuality and begin to work through my parade of issues in that department. He was a police officer and basically a 3-night-stand. I laugh now at my choice of a "uniform/hero" in keeping with my innocent belief in safety and honor under uniform. I would experience the "power of woman" this year as well, in my "new" sexy body. A part of me wished I could have truly waited for a real love, but by that time I was *exploding.* My brother laughed at my guilt.

"I think the fact that you held out until you were 29 more than stops anyone from calling you a slut for sleeping with the guy on the first date!!"

Over the next year, the-police-officer would be followed by the-pathological-liar-from-Oklahoma. And Oklahoma would show me how dishonesty could bring about true devastation. I was in love with the idea of marriage. He left me standing on the side of the road with no money, no home, and no job. I think everyone finds themselves in "Oklahoma" at some time in their learning process. This would be followed by three more years of wandering beyond Oklahoma, and finally the arrival of my 33rd birthday. I had always had an internal knowingness that my thirty-third year in this life would be the key, but I had no idea how accurate and incredible that delivery would be.

The Week That Would Change it All

The Week That Would Change it All

Chapter One

If you have ever hit a point in your life of absolute nothingness, then you will be familiar with the desperation that accompanied my decision to travel to England. The terms *last chance*, and *exhaustion with life* would be other adjectives I would use to describe it. The previous three years in Virginia following the Oklahoma incident had been a succession of attempts to create a life for myself, with one crushing inability to succeed after another. And I finally looked up at God and said…
I've had enough of this life.
I don't want to do this anymore.
I don't see the point.

Keep in mind that at that point I was not considering actual suicide. But I can't express clearly enough how disappointed I was in how my life had turned out by age 33, and rather obviously that downward slide filled with good intentions had begun at age thirty.

In all my life there had been a handful of things I was certain of. The *first* life certainty was a warrior's enthusiasm that I could make a difference in the world; and that there was a large and important destiny I was to fulfill. It went beyond just a hope to be special, as is portrayed by the dramatics of TV and the movies. But at some point in those last few years, that fire had all but died out within me. I initiated project after project as an entrepreneur, or through nonprofit organizations in an attempt to give life the meaning and purpose I had once been so sure of. This included motivational speaking on life and career transitions, work with international relief organizations and the childcare industry, to name a few of the big projects. I gave them all I had and none of the seedlings grew into flowers. So what in the world was I born for? I believe I actually brought the concept of rejection to a whole new level as I was cast out of room after room in different projects.

Now, at this point you must be thinking that I'm not addressing some major personality flaw. Or, at the very least, I have delusions as to the greatness of my contribution, in the face of which the masses are actually fleeing from my presence. To this I can tell you that soul searching and spirit guidance has revealed an obsessive tendency in project focus, but I knew at some level that there was a much larger theme at play. Truthfully, some of these people were throwing me out of rooms before they even interacted with the project in any depth or met me! So I trace the line back three years to the point in time where my life seemed to get de-railed. And it's here that we find the total destruction of my *second* life certainty.

On July 22, 1995 I met a woman who was to become my first Teacher. And was *I* ever a lot of work. I had never heard the word metaphysics before, but a colleague had referred me to this "psychic" for a reading. She was a teacher with many levels of abilities and acted as a metaphysical life counselor. She could channel energy physically to heal, channel her Guides as a medium, and so much more. Sometimes I marvel at her patience over the seven years we were together to bring me from ground zero to the present. She took me on "journey's" to deconstruct and rebuild me. She helped me to see my negative traits clear enough to choose again. That was really her specialty, in addition to aiming me at a broad spectrum of disciplines such as universal law, astrology, feng shui, numerology, chakra balancing, etc.

But our client-teacher relationship was not normal. Even from the beginning. She must have known at multiple levels. Once, I asked her why she had stayed with me for so long, through so much, when others had frustrated her. She said that at my first session she could see how much I really wanted to learn and was honestly asking for assistance.

I am truly honored by every moment we ever spent together. We took a trip to Colorado, met in Washington, DC for a weekend extended session, and spent untold regular hours together in teacher-student sessions over a period of 7-years. She gave me access to speak directly to spirit in natural trance mediumship as time progressed, and I found my most powerful interest in those communications. The ability and gift to give another person a direct line of access to physically converse with the Guides is immense to me. No passion in my life has so moved me. Nothing in life ever seemed so important.

I now understand she is what they call "a natural." A triple Pisces who was born with such immense abilities, that she can use to heal everything she touches. She vibrates with such love that to stand beside her physically puts you in a state of euphoria and calm. This is not to say that she isn't working through lessons and issues of her own; but at some point in our interactions, I believed I had found my destiny.

God had given me the business background, and the Guides channeling through her had confirmed that I was "her other half." And, in fact, we have the exact same astrology chart - only flipped in reverse. At the time, where she was more non-physically oriented in her work, I was detailed and able to organize with great skill. Spirit (her Guides) said we were like yin and yang forming the perfect whole to bring her into the world to serve humanity at a global level. And through all of my fears in life, I trust what comes from Spirit implicitly. And I set off on a road filled with that second life certainty. That working with Spirit Guides is where I belong.

So, perhaps if I had just kept to that global declaration, maybe things would have turned out differently. Though, even as I type that thought, I can see there was a plan, and then a *revised* plan to come *after* my world came crashing down. It actually crashed three times followed by a fourth total dismissal that sent me into the greatest depression of my life. And it can all be summed up in one simple statement:

She didn't want to do it.

Didn't want the publicity. Didn't want to loose the simplicity of her lifestyle and anonymity. Didn't want the responsibility. And who can really blame her. She has total past-life memory of being murdered more than once as she stepped forward publicly. My thoughts about the situation often end with the same notes…

Who can say what another should or should not choose? We can only make choices for ourselves. Anything else would be an inappropriate judgment.

Now, I know the earth plane is a free-will free-choice zone. But, this decision coming from a woman I totally trusted, who had taught me to trust Spirit, left me shocked and lost. I had only one question left for God at that point.

What happens when two people come to earth with a plan to serve humanity and one of the two changes their mind?

So I asked, and asked, and asked. I actually got pretty angry in my private conversations with my maker… truth be told. After three false starts at working together, which all ended in her bailing out, I asked for an independent reading from another internationally renowned metaphysical professional. This reading offered a bit of comfort and heralded the beginning of the end.

In the reading, a soul contract was discovered in the akashic records that revealed what they call a "gray contract." This contract is not a positive one to hang onto. In simple terms, I was personally responsible for halting my Teachers' spiritual growth in a past life. I stood by and allowed her to be killed, and from the guilt of this I would now do anything to help her advance. This left me with a feeling that I could never do enough. So measures were taken to clear this at the soul level so that we could move on.

I thought this was a very positive revealing. To clear the slate in light of the truth is, to me, always positive even if there is initial pain to work through. That was what made my Teachers' reaction surprising. She was angered that I had sought answers elsewhere. I tried to explain that my search for answers was for understanding what *I* was supposed to do with my life from this point forward. But I realize now that this was her exit point with me. And honestly, it was like taking someone who already suffered from orphan syndrome having to be on the physical plane, and having their "mother" disown them.

How could the person I loved so deeply, the one who had taught me everything I believed in, abandon me? Make a choice that directly contradicts the information from the highest soul levels and guides? And with her parting words by telephone that she could not deal with my family's issues, (as if distant relatives she could choose zero interaction with easily were the real reason), she walked out of my life forever.

How could I go on? How could I not agonize and believe I had failed God, humanity and the universe? How could I not have thoughts that I must be a horrible person if someone like her would not work with me?

I chose to have no judgment for her choices, and sought to understand the highest of truths in continuing to "weed my own garden." I hoped that the hurt inside would heal fully and that eventually I would be able to feel good about things. I was to learn a great deal about the "revised plan" at Stansted Hall, and not a moment too soon for this girl wishing to serve who had finally given up.

In the three years that followed my physical departure from Florida, I experienced a near-miss with marriage and motherhood. I traveled across more than half of the United States alone and lost all of my belongings for nearly a year. I lived under the "control" of relatives. Landed in a relationship with a man that didn't bother to tell me he was married. Helped a 21 year-old girl become self-sufficient, who I later found out was nearly a pathological liar. Went from progressing business executive to secretarial pool minimum wage if I worked at all; and in the ensuing struggle at entrepreneurial freedom now stood $58,000 in debt with no job in sight. Virginia became my own personal version of hell. So it won't surprise you when I tell you I put my affairs in order prior to getting on that plane to England. I left financial instructions, keys, and my parakeet with one of my dearest friends. I had had it. And knew I was quite literally leaving nothing behind.

My deal with God for this trip was pretty straight forward:

- If I'm supposed to do something "metaphysical" with my career or life at all, will you please show me what that is.
- If I have any abilities could you please reveal them to me.
- If I am just supposed to sit down and shut up and have an interest in metaphysics as only a hobby, please tell me…because I'm not jumping in and getting my hopes up ever again.

A few months prior to the decision to go and train at Stansted Hall, I had come across a book on one of my wanderings entitled *Born Knowing*, by John Holland. It was a fascinating account of his psychic and mediumistic abilities, as well as training he went through himself at Stansted; and I put this school training on my list-of-things-to-do-before-I-die. If for no other reason, I thought, just for an interesting excursion. This "sign" was followed by the release of the movie X-Men 2, in which a school for the gifted allowed mutants to be accepted and nurtured. As I watched the movie I longed for a new teacher and place to see what I might be. Ironically, Stansted Hall as a building holds a remarkable resemblance to "mutant high." This fact tickled me and made the decision feel even more correct. I was here to learn the truth, and little did I know how large that truth would be.

Chapter Two

I'm not sure exactly when it started…seeing the "faces" and "places" every time I closed my eyes. I'm fairly certain it was within 2 hours of arrival. I took a nap for a little while in the afternoon to combat the jet lag and had strange dreams. It was the reverse of opening your eyes to find some strange guy 6 inches from your face, making you jump out of your skin. I was seeing these strangers and quick snapshots of landscapes and buildings completely foreign to me. It was a little irksome, actually. And I couldn't seem to control it. Even more annoying for someone who likes to be in control. The sensation would grow, and thankfully I would also be graced for the first time in my life with all-important definitions to understand it.

What *you* need to know first and foremost about Stansted, as I discovered, is that at the time I attended it was a very powerful training ground for mediumship and psychic abilities. This comes from years and years of use for *only* this purpose. Drawn from all over the world, gifted souls come and spend 12 hours a day in meditation and classroom interaction. This creates and attracts spectacular levels of energy. It's fantastic, but at the same time it can be a bit frightening. Overall though, I would have to say I had never felt more at home. Once it is explained to you what is happening, as your senses expand to take in this new level, you can not help but be forever changed. Quite honestly, it's very hard to return to the normal world once you have touched this depth and peace. Not to mention how it "opens you up," and those sensitivities then make you too-sensitive to normal every-day things like television violence, radio noise, fluorescent lighting, etc. But I'm getting a bit ahead of myself here, and it's important that I show you the progression of things. I was, after all, entering into this arena just to watch and hoping to learn a little bit to help me cope with a life that seemed to have gone astray. Not so different, perhaps, than you who are reading this book, and wondering many of the same things about trying to live this life given you.

Chapter Three

I saw him first at the dinner table that evening. Walking in 3 hours earlier to the social hour and tea had been incredibly difficult for me. To coin a phrase, I was definitely a stranger in a strange land, and clusters of other students made it obvious that many were returning friends, at ease and at home. I, on the other hand was still wondering what in the world has possessed me to come here. Truthfully, I had no real understanding of what mediumship was, and the first lady I met was no help in uplifting my courage.

"Do you know what the classes are focusing on this week?" she asked *me* (of all people) as she poured sugar in her tea.

"Mediumship and working with guides…I think." I answered her, and to my surprise she got a bit defensive.

"Oh, no. I don't think so. They don't get deeply into that sort of thing here." She stated flatly.

I could have easily bolted or cried at that point. I couldn't believe that thousands of miles around the planet had I traveled to a place full of people that still had less-than-enthusiastic acceptance. Spectacular. So now what do I do?

Luckily, this woman was truly the exception, and not representative of the other 58 students in attendance for the week. Sure, we were all at varying levels in life, but meeting Jane and Paula a few minutes later helped me breathe my first sigh of relief. They were all smiles and British friendliness. We attended the opening orientation together and were to become "tablemates" for all meals throughout the week. First-meal seating became self-assigned tables.

And it was there that I first laid eyes on him. I now find it amusing, and I'm beyond grateful to see that every second at Stansted was part of Spirit's plan and training, whether we were in an actual classroom or not. My guides knew the progression of things I would need to learn and be supported through. And that support and synchronicity was with me in every second.

The British guy's name was Ryan. We had instant attraction to each other which lead from group tabletop banter to me asking him if he would like to take a walk around the grounds after dinner, and before the Sunday Service. I would have to say the evening had an "inevitable destination" that turned into a 4-hour walk and skipping the chapel services. We both seemed to know where the train we were on was headed, though I did my best to resist it. He would help me address my wounded heart and sexuality among other things.

He had spent the last few years in America working on a ranch in New England, exploring parapsychology and how to deal with negative entities. I was definitely attracted to his protective nature and warrior tendencies, but knew that delving into darkness to meet it head on was like joining it in some ways; and I wondered if perhaps he might be here to learn how to use even more light and less drama to assist people dealing with such problems.

At this point, it bears mentioning to anyone reading my constant use of the term "Spirit" and "Guide" what the proper definition is for each. They are *not* the same thing as *ghosts*. A Guide is a non-physical being that walks beside you in this lifetime, through prior agreement before the incarnation began, to assist you. This Guide can be someone you shared a past life with, an ascended master, an animal spirit, a nature spirit, or even a being from the angelic realms. The number of Guides you have with you may change as you reach different points in your life, but there are always a few that never leave your side. I always found this thought comforting, myself.

Now, relatives who have crossed over from this lifetime may also come for a time to be with or assist you, but none of these are "ghosts" either. A ghost is the remnant energy of a being who still lingers on the earth plane and has not completed the crossover. This can be due to their feeling that they need to finish something. It can also be because they hold tremendous anger, or got shocked by the suddenness of their death. Whatever the reason, I need it to be very clear to you what the difference is as we progress. Guides are always assisting us in finding the highest path of love and light for our soul growth. Crossed over relatives can be wonderfully supportive, but I have found are usually vibrating slightly lower on the energetic scale than your primary team of Guides. Ascended Masters, and finally Angels, take the scale even higher. And believe me, there is a different "feel" to conversing with each level.

Returning to the gift of Ryan; our companionship was all part of my healing process. I would have to say I couldn't have gotten through the week without him. The first two nights he slept in my room with great patience and protectiveness for my process. Leading me past old sexual and relationship barriers and bearing witness, also, to several strange events in the realization of my abilities.

Remember…every interaction was a "set-up." Each occurrence was a link in an important progression of events that had to be handled very carefully… so that I did not implode at any point of the awakening.

Chapter Four

On the first evening at Orientation we were introduced by the course leader to himself and the five additional "tutors" as they are called in England. We listened to each of them speak a bit about the type of instruction they would be providing training in, and then each student, in turn introduced themselves to the group and selected which primary class they would like to be a part of. There was a beginning metaphysics and psychic development class, two advanced and platform mediumship classes for currently practicing mediums, an energy class, an art class and a trance mediumship class. It was the last one aimed specifically at trance mediumship that I knew was my proper destination. And as I sat the next morning in my first circle and gazed at the other twelve people in the room, I shivered from both excitement and the strange coldness inherent in the Library.

They had warned us to dress warmly for this room, but now I was beginning to understand why they had laughed while saying it. The library wasn't just *temperature* cold. It was *spirit* cold. Apparently, as it was explained to us, in the dim lighting and cold, spirit has the ability to manifest most strongly, and this is what is necessary for deeper altered states. My enthusiasm was growing and compounded by the fact that it was actually difficult *not* to shift into trance and altered states in the energy of this room. Which brought us to classroom rule number one...we were not to slide into trance if it was not our turn, or instructed to do so. How amusing, and what wonderful potential seemed to exist here to experience the states of consciousness that had always seemed elusive at home. I had about given up on being able to do *anything* deep myself. But perhaps, this place would prove different.

The tutor for this class was a wonderfully soft-spoken woman of motherly energies. I said a little thank-you prayer that she wasn't a dictator, as I needed, I knew, a gentle teacher to feel safe with in such a new environment.

As much as I was filled with enthusiasm, I would have to admit to being equally as nervous. I couldn't wait for the library-trance class times which were intermixed between lectures, meditations, meals and the all-important British tea time. Definitions of the varying types of abilities started the training that week. This was followed by a meditation in which our tutor sent us into what is termed "The Power of Trance." This allowed her time with each of our personal guide-teams to receive specific instructions about what each of us needed for the week.

Fantastic and powerful does not begin to describe this amazing process, and her own ability provided the ultimate instructor in the ideal training ground. In every moment she could "see" and hear her Guides, our Guides, and our energetic process. This is SO important in the classroom environment for learning! I had never been with a teacher who could explain how to use and understand my own abilities. Not to mention that I'd pretty much never had confirmation before this that I even *had* any. I was very excited to do this first exercise and hear what the Guides had to say.

At this point, let me give you a few of those all-important definitions I mentioned earlier so that you can follow along with the information I was about to receive.

Clairvoyance is defined as "clear seeing." It is the ability of a person to perceive flashes of visual images in the *minds eye* through the *third eye* located in the center of the forehead. I thought the definition of a clairvoyant was someone who saw movie-images of future events. But Spirit can communicate with a psychic that receives in this fashion all day long, even conversationally as it is needed. In fact, as symbol is the highest form of communication that exists in the universe, this is a handy ability to have.

I was told very specifically and pointedly that I was clairvoyant.

I should have guessed I suppose. But I had always thought that being raised on huge doses of television that I just had a very vivid fantasy-life and imagination. I can recall thinking more than once as I grew up how grateful I was for this. When life got tough, I would retreat into an entire other world. As it turns out, that while some of this was creative visualization and fantasyland, a bunch of it was not.

You are the ultimate example of a being that lives in this world but is not of it.

This saying had always been a favorite of mine. It felt so true, but I had actually considered that I was just inappropriately being ego-centered, bent on escapism, and wishing to be a better-than-everyone else kind-of "special." Now I see that it's O.K. It's just truth. I had sat in a circle once about two years ago, and I recall that the medium at one point had stopped his presentation to stare at me.

"You know," he said with a strange look on his face as he pointed to me where I was seated in the center of the room, "You're shifting continuously inter-dimensionally…did you know that?"

Of course, it rang true when he said it, but once again I had always chalked it up to daydreaming and fantasyland. By the time I would finish at Stansted for this week, I would understand much more fully the concept of altered states of awareness and what each level feels like. Truth-be-told, the altered states I was born with the ability to access are so much lighter in feel and more pleasant than day-to-day conscious living, it's no wonder I prefer to literally "zone-out." But now it was time to do this with purpose and focus rather than escapism.

All Mediums are psychic, but not all psychics are Mediums. You, are both.

To continue with our definitions, we get to other psychic abilities in addition to clairvoyance. There is *clairaudience* (subjective and objective), *clairsentience, knowing, clair-smelling* and *clair-tasting* (these last two being our class's funny terminology).

Objective clairaudience is when you can hear spirit in a voice other than your own either in your head or in the room. *Subjective clairaudience* is when you hear spirit talking in your head, but it sounds like your own voice. It turns out I have the subjective version of the ability. I would dare to say more people have experienced this more than they realize, but dismissed it as just their own thought process. As I had done myself over the years.

Clairsentience means "clear feeling." Most people will allow for the use of this ability. It's when you "sense" someone is there. At one time, while sitting in a session with my first teacher about five years prior, I had the rare experience of my abilities being pointed out. She and I had been in deep conversation, when quite unconsciously I had turned my head away from her to look across the room in an entirely different direction. By the time I had turned my head back again to look at her she had stopped talking and was sitting there staring at me with a funny smile on her face.

"Do you know what you just did?" She asked me.

When I stared at her blankly she informed me that I had just turned to look at/recognize several Guides that had just entered the room. This fact had both fascinated and frustrated me. So I really could "see" them but not in the manner I desired for conversational purposes?? Great. Frustrating for years. But that frustration was about to be lifted a bit.

Clair-smelling or *clair-tasting*, I'm quite certain has the true technical term *olfactory sensing*, but we turned it into our own vocabulary for convenience. Spirit has the ability to manipulate energy to generate a smell in the room or taste in the mouth. I've experienced the smelling on occasion. Gardenias are said to herald an angelic presence. Or a spirit guide may notify you of their presence by the smell of a spice.

I have worked with many students and clients and recognize the frustration that many people face. They don't realize that God, their higher self and/or their Guides do not have some secret code book that they must learn before communication can begin.

Symbols and signs that are of greatest knowledge and meaning *to the individual* are used for this process. It is certainly most helpful to study a variety of true symbols for which you have an affinity. But the process can be likened to creating your very own mental dictionary. During one communication at Stansted in a trance mediumship demonstration, one of the Guides said, *"It would be so wonderful if you would talk to us more…and even more wonderful if you would listen to the answers."*

For an excellent movie version of how Guides work with you, I recommend you watch the movie *City of Angels* with Nicolas Cage. I knew when I saw this for the first time that it was an example of how our Guides are right there in the room with us at all times. They use energy and telepathy and emotion to help us. And this realization brings us to the definition of *knowing* as a psychic sense. Though I don't think there is any lengthy definition actually required for this particular ability, it does bear mentioning that most people override this natural instinct and cause themselves undue hardship.

Knowingness is a message from your higher self. We mentalize and stress over life on a daily basis and wonder how to make the highest choices. I have heard so often from students,

"How do I know what God's plan is? How do I know what path to take?"

Knowingness is honestly the best guidance floating around. We come close to using it properly when we are told to "follow our gut feeling" because our true communication center with the higher self resides in the region of the body known as the solar plexus. It's frustrating that our society actually says we must use mental logic alone in decision-making, when instead a combination of both with a foundation on intuition would make for a much less painful earthly experience. Truth is actually not hidden from us; many are just playing the game of life with an inaccurate rule book.

The definition of mediumship vs. these psychic abilities came next for me, and mercifully so, since I was in the process of learning I *was* one and that came with a bit of fear from false stories. A medium is not something that just anyone can learn to be. It is an ability you must be born with as part of your life plan.

The best way to see how this works is to look at a scale from one to twelve. *One* is the level at which normal waking consciousness interacts. Two people sitting at a table talking is a demonstration of this. We'll say Spirit/Guides are vibrating at a level *twelve* frequency for the purposes of this example. They are standing right next to the table and people in the room, but they are not perceived. A medium is born with the ability to move into an altered state of consciousness from level one to level six. Spirit dials their frequency down from level twelve to level six to meet the medium on the inner *mental planes*. It is there that a *blending* occurs for communication.

Mental mediumship and platform mediumship are, as I would describe it, eyes-open translation of the conversation. The medium is linked in to both worlds and has their eyes open. Trance mediumship is an eyes-closed deeper altered state whereby a medium can get greater focus or even allow spirit to use their vocal cords or body. I should make it clear at this point that there is never anything even close to possession going on for these processes. Each medium has a primary "Control" guide that acts as gatekeeper and protector. The medium has full free-will authority at all times, and the blending occurs in *consciousness* not bodily possession.

It also is important to mention at this point that mediumship is not a dramatic circus show. This work is powerfully important to assist humanity in understanding the truth of how life functions, and Spirit will never participate in dramatics or theatrics. Should shaking occur briefly or odd sounds, it is because the blending process is not in the perfect alignment, and the powerful energies it requires to accomplish this communication are in the process of being adjusted and harmonized. Mediumship is different each time based on a wide variety of internal and external factors that must be dealt with. If the medium is tired or stressed, the energy needed may not be strong enough or focused enough to accomplish the linking.

I would have to say from my perspective that it is a plenty dramatic enough miracle to hear a completely different voice come through a trance medium's vocal cords. And this, when done appropriately is very authentic. But beware the authenticity of a medium that flops about like a fish and launches into multiple accents in their own voice. As it was explained to us, this is important business. Spirit is not about to diminish you or themselves in ridiculous theatrics. In a real demonstration, even the most basic individual will be aware of very different and powerful energies in the room.

Chapter Five

These first entrées to sit in what they term "The Power of Trance" were fascinating to me. I entered as I would into any meditation, but soon discovered that there was definitely a different depth involved. I fought it at first, thinking I was loosing control and falling inappropriately to sleep. Twice, I "awoke" and thought I was about to fall out of my chair. The next time I "came around" to discover my head had gone down to have my chin on my chest and I was drooling.

"Spectacular..." I though with embarrassment. And I said a silent prayer to get through the week unscathed by any monumentally embarrassing events.

But this was my shot. It was my time to have access to answers. So I learned quickly to ask questions and share what was happening to me in all of the exercises.

"You're not falling asleep darling," our Tutor informed me in her soft British accent. "You are releasing normal stream of thought and surrendering within the Power. It allows your Guides to work on you."

After the major session I had mentioned previously, whereby our Tutor had her own conversations with each team of Guides, my world was to implode emotionally. If you recall, I had just spent a very long 3 years of life difficulties. As Ryan seemed to have been sent in to assist with the healing of certain wounds, the Guides were now poised to release the flood gates necessary to heal the rest of what I would call "the mess."

A child spirit guide, a little girl, and an "angel" were brought to my attention. I was surprised by this, though it's funny how you can see in hind-sight how I already knew it. My first teacher had told me that no one can ever tell you who your Guides are, and if they do, they are being dishonest. But this is not entirely true by my experience. In reality, I believe that yes, there are important details and knowingness that appropriately comes only to the individual and is then confirmed as part of the growth process. On the other hand, when the time is right for knowingness to be brought from subconscious to conscious light, I believe the Guides can initiate that at the divine perfect time through any appropriate channel. And this can most pointedly occur by mutual soul decision through a medium.

For my part, I was aware of several animal and masculine guides, but the declaration of an angel who was *female* was a bit new for the *personality* of me to grasp. I believe I have always turned mentally to the masculine to feel an archetypal sense of protection in a world that seemed to me overwhelmingly hostile.

The awareness of the little girl brought up an entirely different range of emotions and sense of guilt. When three years ago I had made the difficult decision to have an abortion, I had been aware of the spirit of a little girl that intended to come through. She and I had talked at length, as I agonized over finding myself without money, a home, or partner. Aside from emptying my bank accounts and being dishonest, this man from Oklahoma would not be around. I couldn't exactly hear her side of the conversations at that point, but I hoped that she could understand my decision. I knew at the time I absolutely was not to proceed with the pregnancy. And eight years into the future it would be revealed to me that had I had this child; it would have been a terrible disaster that lead to my premature death in this life.

As the exercise continues, the Tutor proceeded to tell me (and I noticed no one else), that *she had been told I was coming* to Stansted. I have to admit to an ego thrill at the special-ness that this fact might hold. The thrill didn't last too long though in the face of the daunting "responsibility" inherent in the fact though. In the next few moments of information delivery I went to pieces emotionally when she said that in the last years I had been literally crushed, and it was necessary to come here, in part to heal.

In spite of my best efforts to not cry in front of 12 strangers in the middle of the class, I couldn't keep up the thin wall that held back the reality. I vaguely remember her holding me and saying softly, "It's O.K. daring…. everyone understands…..this is why we've come here…you're not the only one."

Once the worst of it had passed, and I was back to some semblance of composure, the rest of the information was translated.

I needed to feel good about myself.

I needed to learn to protect myself because there are those who will try to misuse my powers.

The Tutor was given a specific tutorial for me for the week.

I am clairvoyant.

I have been using my motivational public speaking career to hide.

And so it began. Apparently this was not just going to be a cute little metaphysical week of fun facts and tools.

Chapter Six

In the out-of-classroom "classrooms" as I jokingly refer to the time and interactions surrounding the more formal lesson plans, other interesting occurrences were shaping the face of my training.

During the first two nights, I was incredibly grateful to have Ryan in my room. I was shaken from awareness at more levels than I could even bring to consciousness, and glad for the companionship and delivery into the arms of a man with patience.

For starters, there were two twin beds in the room, and I migrated back and forth. Having never been married and used to sleeping alone, I would at times need my own space. On the other hand, with Spirit so active in both etheric *and* physical ways, I was at other times more in need of being held than I can ever recall. At one point on the first night I was shocked awake by the sensation as if a spirit had dropped right through the ceiling, through my chest and through the floor beneath me. And before the week was out, I would be amused at the actual sight of white etheric energy swirling across the ceiling. I was thrilled by the "ha-ha Ghostbusters" experience of it all, but disturbed as well.

On the second night came a larger occurrence. Ryan awoke to find me standing perfectly still in the center of the room in the twelve inches or so between the beds. He spoke to me, and when he received no response, reached out and touched my thigh.

Never have I experienced *anything* like the sheer shock of what happened next. I had not been aware of myself, and when he touched me and said my name I came slamming like lightning back into my body. I truly, in that instant, had absolutely no idea where I was. I let out a scream and when I regained my bearings discovered I was shaking violently. It all must have frightened the daylights out of Ryan who had the common sense not to touch me again, but instead just keep speaking softly to reassure me.

It was baffling to me how I could have not known I was standing up, or why the shaking was so severe. I apologized to Ryan profusely and after a bit of it had subsided, went to the bathroom and returned to be held for the next several hours.

Over breakfast with my tablemates on that first morning I had sheepishly asked if any of them had "slept weird." Many of them being returning students, broke into laughter at the question posed by the little American girl.

"Why do you ask sweetheart?" Jane had giggled over her eggs. "Experiencing some new things are you?"

Welcome to Stansted Hall was the theme of the discussion that followed. I couldn't stop laughing at the stories of other peoples interactions with Spirit. At one point in their darkened room, Jane and Paula had had first a kind discussion with a particularly persistent spirit followed by a more insistent declaration from Paula to "piss off." It was all told in a very British way that had us laughing until our sides hurt.

For me, above all, the support and interaction at meal time proved to be a fantastic balancing point to discuss things, laugh to lighten seriousness, and feel again supported. Nearly everything about Stansted felt like home. It was such a relief to have answers and gain understanding. To discover that I'm not alone and I'm not a crazy person.

Back in the library for class with our primary Tutor, I shared when it was my turn the experience of the shocking night prior. She turned her head slightly, as she always did when listening to her Guides explain the answer to my inquiry, and she came back to me with a question.

"Darling, do you usually walk in your sleep?" she asked.

"No." I answered flatly. Though there had been once a very long time ago I had awoken standing in my bedroom with a picture in my hands, taken from the wall.

She conversed again with Spirit and returned with a smile, "Do you live alone?"

"Yes."

"Then how would you know?"

I was instantly disturbed by the ramifications of what she implied, and dismissed her. The thought of my wandering in my underwear beyond my control around the apartment complex parking lot was not an image I desired to conjure. I was told at some point that this occurred to attend to bodily needs like going to the bathroom or getting something to eat, while a person was in the sleep state and journeying astrally to work with their Guides. I honestly didn't care to even go *that* far, since I was certain they were mistaken where I was concerned.

Moving on from the question-time into the exercise of the day, I was at my usual ready-point while trying not to submit to the strong trance energies of the room. Everything was honestly so new to me, from the soft-spoken-ness of my classmates with multiple accents (I'm used to American loudness), to each impending exercise. I found myself constantly trying to keep up.

While I was busying myself with these adjustments, I watched as the Tutor checked in with several of my classmates. By now I was starting to figure out that with the exception of myself and the guy sitting next to me, everyone else seemed to be quite advanced. They had worked in trance or as healers and mediums before. Most could "see" as well as the instructor, though each in their own way, the guides present. I wished I too was operating at such a level, and simply resigned myself to watching everyone and doing my best to "let go" in each exercise and hopefully allow spirit to work with me a little too.

It seemed that the Tutor was taking some sort of a vote, and making notations in her notebook of those that did not desire to have spirit/their Guides "speak" through them in trance. For some reason I thought that this was for an end-of-the-week interactive. That would be cool, I thought, to get to see a trance demonstration. I noticed that she did not ask me, which wasn't too surprising. After all, this wasn't something that I actually knew how to *do*.

So she finished her questions, closed her notebook and said, "O.K. everyone, are we ready?"

I'm sure the look on my face was priceless. *We're doing this now?! Yikes.*

I murmured something akin to "and we're off" as I assumed the position, palms up to enter into the Power of Trance exercise.

I knew almost immediately that this was going to be different. I started to shiver, from more than the cold. It was a bit reminiscent to the shaking from the previous night when Ryan touched me, but it was a slow build this time rather than a shocking jolt.

Deeper and deeper we went as I strained to stop the shaking sensation which probably felt more visible than it actually was.

"Teacher said we mustn't flop around like fishes.....no drama...."

I was thinking this at the same time I was stalwartly determined to breathe and re-center myself. But ironically, each time I declared peace, calm and centeredness in my mind, the shaking intensified. Truth-be-told I was a bit irked at both my inability to "behave," and the way it might distract me from the really fascinating things to be witnessed as they occurred around the room.

And begin to occur they did.

To my right and all the way around to the beginning of the circle beside the teacher, sat a pair of twins that worked together. One was the anchor, the other the channel. Having a "watcher" and energy anchor is seriously required for a public practicing trance medium due to the dangers inherent in practicing this ability. It was a good thing that I didn't know too much about this yet, but I'd learn as things progressed.

The twin, at this point, who acts as the medium for a spirit guide that alters both her voice and breathing, began to speak. Of what was said, I remembered one thing that was to become very important to me.

A Spirit Guide/entity may wait thousands of years for the one medium capable of "holding" them.

I thought this was very wonderful, and such an honor it must be.

As I continued to struggle with my increased shaking, I remember alternately thinking: *Wow, that was cool, now I get to listen to someone else do it....*

And before me she stood.

The Tutor had moved across the room to stand in front of *me*. And from my not so centered perspective with eyes appropriately closed, I found it interesting to note that I consciously seemed to be slightly out of my body and shifted to my back right by perhaps a few inches.

Holy Shit...you've got to be kidding me...
Was all I could think as the knowingness that my time had come helped me find enough determination to attempt to allow it.

"There is a friend here with her that wishes to speak..." the instructor said, with an additional soft array of encouraging remarks to the Guide I could feel so powerfully moving through me. That was the way it worked apparently. With encouragement from the teacher and the energetic assistance of the circle, a Guide can be assisted in finding the right balance with their medium. Or at least that's how this particular first encounter was transpiring.

At this point I was shaking, and tears flowed down my cheeks. It was the most powerful of emotions to feel the attempt at this merger. I was scared and thrilled equally. I really wanted to allow this. But could I?

I continued to hear the Tutor's coaxing, and her voice sounded quite far away to my ears. She wasn't talking to me anyway, and I suddenly felt like I was going to throw up. But it wasn't nausea. It was more like the overwhelming urge that you must speak, but with no idea what you're going to say. So I just let it happen.

"She has fear..."
It sounded like someone else's voice to my ears. Filled with a beauty in harmonics like nothing I have ever experienced. But it was shaky as this entity attempted the alignment required. Like a radio station not quite tuned into the station.

"I understand. Move through your medium's emotion." It was the Tutor again. Speaking to the "Angel".

Yes...it was the Angel, I suddenly knew. Through the shaking it felt like comforting wings surrounded me from behind. Then she responded to the Tutor's instruction and a peaceful center expanded from my solar plexus like a pebble dropped in a pool. It helped me center enough to allow the next bit of communication through.

"She is loosing time, and does not believe you," the Angel said through my vocal cords to the instructor in a stronger and even more harmonically beautiful voice.

"What can I do to help your Medium?" she asked her.

"She does not know how to live this life...if you could help her...she is looking for a mother..."

At the realization of the truth of my sorrow and sadness, both with my life and the abandonment I felt at the exit of my first teacher, I nearly fell apart. Tears flowed, and I realized I was crying now and shaking more violently. There was so much love inherent in this Angel's presence. I vaguely heard the Tutor thanking her and saying that she understood. I felt the Angel withdraw her full impact as she eased back gently.

Like from very far away I heard her say my name. "…..you're O.K. darling….she didn't hurt you." The instructor spoke, now directly to me for the first time. "She is a being of such pure love that you are not used to merging and holding her, so you are feeling it all as emotion."

Amidst the shaking and tears within my deeply altered state, I was also aware of powerful energies in assistance. Some were from my classmates and Tutor; other energies flowed from several of my Guides as they moved to re-balance me. I was told later, by those who can "see" her, that she is more beautiful than can be imagined as she rises up behind me. Constantly, I know now, she is with me.

During my own personal drama, which continued for 30 minutes or so, others in the room were experiencing their own awakenings and callings. Some were inspired to move as healers as another student, Sarah did for me. Others brought through Guides that were new to them. It was a safe and powerful forum for this. Profound, I would say, for us all in some way.

Chapter Seven

Sarah stayed with me through dinner. To say I was still altered would probably have been an understatement. But I was doing my best to function. Ordered to eat chocolate cake to offset the sugar drain from the trance-interaction, you'd think I'd have been thrilled. But on the whole I was very nauseous. If you recall, I said I was glad not to have all of the mental details and definitions for what transpires during such an event. This proved to be part of Spirit's plan for my training.

To get me through my first trance-merge at least once from what I would term "ground zero," it had to be a surprise. Otherwise, I would have mentally gotten in the way. The shaking I experienced was actually physical shock to the body. It is equivalent to call-a-paramedic trauma shock. But additionally, for a medium, there are other severe dangers. A medium in an altered state must *never* be touched. The psychic shock of this can even manifest physically with a burning of the skin, or worse can actually *kill* the medium. This suddenly brought the entire episode into greater clarity for me. Our Tutor had asked my permission for Sarah to touch me to help me get grounded. My permission had negated some of the possible shock, but still caused the nausea. And the night previous, Ryan and the sleep-walking wake-up had been to demonstrate both the losing-of-time *and* the shock. I was starting to feel like a crash-test dummy. So much for my plan to just *watch*.

And Spirit was just getting started. I departed the dinning room and headed up to my room after dinner. I wasn't up to the extra art class for the evening, and Ryan had been "removed," setting off for the evening to visit friends in another town. I was O.K. with being by myself for the first time overnight. I had a lot to discuss with my guides, and craved the solitude anyway. Though, I think solitude is a ridiculously inaccurate definition for the next seven hours of interaction....

I was definitely tired. But the events of the day had opened me up, and I wasn't going to let the opportunity slip past me to have the one-on-one communication with my Guides that I'd craved my entire life. That "subjective clairaudience" thing was in full gear, and I let the conversations *fly*. I wanted to know...*why didn't you guys tell me...why so much life gone by without doing this*.... And one guide at a time, we talked.

It began with the "Angel." Then there was the little brown-haired girl. There were many tears. It was time I needed desperately. They were wonderful. I had put on music, and an interesting thing transpired. Through an odd and powerful array of music I don't think I'd ever listened to before, came answers. Answers in perfect succession to the questions and interactions. It was haunting and profound. It could never have been negated as "coincidence" by even the angriest or most rational mind. And I flowed with it. Said what I had to say.

The meetings with the angel and girl-child lead me onward. I had wondered why my Tutor had not identified the primary soul group guides I had felt with me for years. She had brought to my attention the two, so at some point in my conversation I was ready to dismiss the others as my being incorrect.

Dating back to work with my first teacher, a series of realizations had brought me to a profound meeting and intensely personal confirmation. Though I work with many guides from many places and time periods, it was confirmed that my soul group is "David" of the Twelve Tribes. We are the warriors. And I can resonate fully with that. But now, here at Stansted, I wondered if I might have been incorrect. With that thought, in the deepest of meditations as I sat in my moonlight filled room....they came.

Twelve riders on horseback appeared. I found myself standing somewhere in a vast desert, at the edge of a bonfire. The night was filled with stars, but my attention was focused on the horses and riders. The silver inlays over black bridles and saddles, and flowing clothing. They had come to solidify the bond. One rider from each of the twelve tribes. And I knew the presence of my father instantly as he dismounted and came to embrace me. *David*. And I felt my undeniable lineage.

At this point I would have to point out through all of the magnificence of what was happening that this knowledge is not of the ego. In fact, it is daunting and humbling and on most days incredibly irrelevant when the alarm clock goes off and my personality has to work an 8 to 5 job on the physical plane. Everyone wishes to be a "special princess" and many through delusions of grandeur believe they were Cleopatra or Queen Elizabeth in a past life. This is used as a tool of the ego to assert a demand for attention from others and gain love and respect not given to the self. For me, I recognize that powerful assistance comes to support me through a life that will require from me much responsibility. Light workers are not sent into comfortable cozy rooms… they are sent into the dark places. I have no time for the pull of my ego, but hopefully enough courage to do what this life will require.

I stood and talked with him for awhile there in the desert. I can see now how these interactions have allowed me later to identify each guide presence once I was thrown back into the "real world." Each Guide *feels* different, *speaks* differently. My "father" is quick and pointed in his discussion, leaving no time to doubt the communication. The Angel is softer. In these beginning days I heard and felt her primarily from behind me over my left shoulder, and often clairvoyantly "saw" wings as a symbol of presence.

All in all it was an important and spectacular evening that lasted from about 7:30 to 9:00pm I would guess, before I fell asleep. But my resting was short-lived. I awoke with a start at about 11:00pm with an absolute urgency to get out of bed. A trip to the bathroom, then a bowl of granola cereal to address the hunger pangs, was followed by a bizarre need for *movement*. With my CD player now belting out an array of 80's and 90's music, I stretched and moved and sang along for about thirty minutes. It felt good, and seemed to bring me into a comfort zone of relaxation to go back to bed. It also is a fact that movement and singing raise the energy in a room for spirit to "work." A fact I did not really know at the time.

As is the style in many European guest rooms, there was a sink which I found to be a wonderful addition for privacy. I had proceeded to brush my teeth and begin to wind down when the next overpowering impulse hit me.

Clear off the bed.

I would say it was more of a *demand* spoken in my head than anything else, and all I could quite sarcastically think to myself as I considered the "request," was that *now* I was developing obsessive-compulsive tendencies to alleviate emotional discomfort.

"Great," I muttered under my breath, abandoning my plan to brush my teeth and reorganizing suitcase, clothing and other articles off of the second twin bed and into a corner closet area. It only took a minute or two, and I was back at the sink with toothbrush in hand.

I would call it a presence. Clairsentience followed closely by clairvoyance as I caught a movement out of the corner of my right eye in the direction of the door to the room. It had not opened, but none-the-less I found myself staring at a very large animal that wandered in casually, took the center path, and climbed up onto the bed I had just cleared.

I resumed furiously brushing my teeth.

Surely I had lost my mind.

Absolutely I must be having a fantasy brought on by stress and lack of sleep.

But when I turned back to the bed, there she laid. I've come to understand that the difference between clairvoyantly "seeing" something and having a "fantasizing moment" is that when you look away – eyes open – then back again, what you thought you "saw" will still be there.

And indeed, there she was. The most gorgeous black jaguar I'd ever seen. An easy 6-feet in length not including the tail. And she was *totally* at ease.

I closed my eyes again and leaned forward on the sink.

"What in the world is *that*…" I asked out loud to no one in particular, and heard the answer clearly in my head.

Look at your watch.

It was exactly midnight.

A cascade of realizations were dawning on me at this point, not the least of which included the fact that I am constantly awakened near the midnight hour and often again at around three in the morning. The three A.M. wakeup is usually a requirement to eat something. I've faced constant ridicule from my family about this eating in the middle of the night. I can see that in some instances it might have been miss-balanced emotional eating, but now, the fact that heavy "journeying" and trance mediumship require "replenishment" was occurring to me very strongly.

I heard myself say the animal's name, as I realized what it was, out loud, and felt the confirmation of truth run the length of my body.

She is your journeying companion, your guardian.

Oh. *Right*…the night journeying and the wake-up call times. Plus this concept of *loosing time* that the Angel had talked about. So they were clarifying that I had powerful companionship and was not wandering the streets in my underwear. I was definitely comforted a bit more about that whole situation.

She is a shape-shifter.

I heard them say it and halted in finishing up the whole tooth-brushing-thing for about the fifth time. "*What* did you say?" I demanded a repeat, but knew I had heard it correctly. "What in God's name could she *possibly* turn into that would be more impressive than *a six-foot jaguar?!*"

I had raised my voice on that last part, and hoped that the rooms' walls were thick enough to hold the array of conversations and weird behaviors I was exhibiting for the night. I had no desire to wake up the world.

I proceeded a bit more quietly with my guessing game at that point.

"She turns into a Man?"

No.

"She turns into a Woman?"

No.

"Fine, I give up."

She turns into you.

And I was frozen again at the words spoken. It's funny how hearing the truth can do that. How it can cause you to go absolutely *still*. A clairvoyant flash and vision filled my minds eye and I remembered that often when I go running for exercise I would "imagine" the physical companionship of the large cat. Her presence would be more than an along-side walk. I would feel her within my body, and as we merged I would run on all fours, sometimes leaving this plane entirely. *No*, I did not do this *literally* so a bystander would see it happen. But happen often it did….and I would loose track of time…..

Yikes.

I slammed back to focus on the room. Like amazing puzzle pieces the elements were starting to come together. Apparently, all of the voices in my head weren't just my own, and the "fantasies" were realities.

Chapter Eight

At the breakfast table, it amazed me to find my usual companions were having a more difficult time waking up than I was. On the whole I was quite peaceful and ready for what the day might bring.

After breakfast was the one-hour guided meditation held in the large hall with the big windows that overlooked the gardens and grounds. I sought the companionship for this exercise with only my guides. I almost felt like I was in a wonderful bubble, and preferred to hold it as long as I could. I can't say for sure if I called her, or if she appeared first and then I became aware of her, but my guardian jaguar came to lie at my feet. It humored me as I sat in the front row to the right of the podium that, everyone gave me a very unusual wide berth. I smiled to note that not only did no one sit in the row with me or behind me, but no one was "sitting on my really big cat" either. Considering the abilities in this group, I wondered if anyone else could actually see her. When the meditation was over, a woman I had never met rushed up to me. She simply glowed with enthusiasm, like a child who had been told a secret and was bursting to tell.

"You are going to be an amazing and wonderful Medium," she whispered and touched my hand. Then as quickly as she appeared, she scurried off.

Now, lest there be a misconception at this point about groups like this coming together to embark on Spiritual truth and awakenings, let me notify you now that it can also be fraught with difficulties. The energies magnify, emotional "buttons" get pushed, and everyone brings the best and worst of their personality traits along for the ride. Sometimes we are open and allow truth to change us in beautiful ways, and other times we sink further into resistance and ego; possibly even lashing out at each other. I would definitely say we had a multitude of all of it going around.

I wasn't the only one brought to an emotional explosion as healing occurred through necessity, and trauma was released. Others I interacted with seemed to sit on the threshold of great ability that they flat out refused to allow. Still others misused or attacked the abilities of classmates and teachers, or rudely caused disruptions in the work being done. If nothing else, I could feel the unsettledness when it happened. I'd say it manifested as "a disturbance in the force," as one Star Wars character used to put it. Spirit would have difficulty getting through it, because negativity of any kind breaks down the continuity of the higher energies.

I, myself, would retreat when necessary to the gardens and woods that surrounded Stansted Hall. I have always been attuned with nature and animals, and at this point in my training found it not only comforting, centering and energizing, but also amazing to be able to continue "hearing" and carrying on discussions with my Guides. I came to love my walks in between classes. Sometimes alone, and sometimes shared.

On one such occasion I walked with Ryan. It was a discussion where I was more teacher than companion on the subject of Universal Law. He, too, had life decisions to make, and when all was complete for the week, he would not even be returning to his life in the United States. British by birth he would choose to stay in England to wander on his private path. My time with him was a great gift, but not to last, as we lived such different lives.

Another walk I participated in, I believe, by direct request of my Guides. It was a powerful important thing, though it made me quite nervous to be a messenger in the delivery of information to another.

I have only met, to my knowledge, three others who are of my soul group. This girl was the first. Her name is Heidi, and I found her in the library class. On the night of "meeting" the riders of the twelve tribes, I at some point was inspired to ask my father if my current Tutor was from my soul group also. I received a definite "no." Taking the conversation a bit further I was told that even my brother in this lifetime, though I had thought perhaps he was, is not of my soul group. That came as a bit of a surprise to me at the time. I think now I realize, though, that what I wanted my brother to be both *for* me and *with* me, is actually different than who and what he has chosen as we have reached adulthood. I love him, but out paths have definitely diverged-in-the-woods, as they say.

Now, however, the Guides were bringing Heidi to my attention. Truthfully, as I got to know her a bit in our classroom circle I found her to be one of the most breathtakingly beautiful creatures I had even encountered. Don't misunderstand this statement, though. Yes, her pretty red hair and soft demeanor are a part of it, but it goes beyond that to things I can't even put a conscious label on. And it didn't seem to matter how many times I asked the question either mentally or by kinesiology, I always got a solid "yes."

So, they wanted me to tell her.

As if I wasn't having enough difficulty negotiating facts for myself. I waited a day or so, and with the confirmations stronger, and Heidi's permission, we took the walk. I'd have to say I'm so grateful I did. It was haunting to discover that though she lived on another continent, the similarities of our life paths had been almost an exact duplicate. Our work, personal difficult life decisions, and current financial status matched. She even had incredible synchronicity with the name "David" as I had. I will always be eternally grateful for this meeting of a sister, and hope that our paths will lead us back together someday. For quite awhile after our time at Stansted I had dreams about her, and feel there was a strong chance we'd been "getting together" outside of the physical plane realities.

In the midst of classes, relationships and realizations, I was grateful to get a little one-on-one private consultation myself. I had scheduled two private sessions. The first was most important to me, as it was with my primary trance instructor. There were tons of questions beginning to surface for me surrounding, most importantly, what in Gods-name was I supposed to do when I returned to the United States!? I had literally left nothing behind. I had no clients, few friends, no happy family relationships in the area left since my brother and I had been shattered apart by his decision to stay in a relationship with a woman my Guides were now telling me to stay away from… and the list went on. After three years of trying to build a business in Virginia, and survive the misfire to Oklahoma, I now stood with upwards of $55,000 of credit card debt and no idea what to do. I was angry. At myself, though I don't know how I could have seen to do anything different; at God for not being clearer, sooner; at a life I had no desire to return to. And the Guides knew it. In some ways, at greater depth than I did.

They began it with a definitive acknowledgement that it had been three years, and then followed that up with a glimpse at the "why."

"Three years ago something happened that caused your higher self and Guides to realize that the original life plan decided upon in the beginning was not going to work." My tutor had recited, with eyes closed as we sat alone in the library. "Something happened to derail you and send you in another direction. They had to make a major adjustment, and knew there was just enough, though barely enough, time to accomplish what they must with you. That is why you now find yourself at Stansted. You are undergoing the most intensive training imaginable; likened to five years in five days. So you understand darling that you are in the most advanced class there is?"

I apologized at that point, my head still spinning with the realization that almost three years to the day I had decided to leave Orlando and follow some guy to Oklahoma. I wanted to throw up at the thought of the potential stupidity inherent in that decision. I knew though that it had come on the heels of something bigger set in motion: the first declaration that my "teacher" would not be my partner. One of these occurrences, or both, could have been the derail point they spoke of. And I was not going to blame myself for my first teacher's exit. That decision and her other behaviors had been her own.

Returning to my tutor's last statement about being in the advanced class, I offered to withdraw and find a more appropriate beginners class. She smiled warmly at my confusion and stepped up to clarify herself.

"No darling, you misunderstand. You are exactly where you are supposed to be. They told me to expect you. You are not here to learn how to do any of this; you already know how to do it *all*. This is just to help you remember what you are capable of."

At this point my personality was stunned. The knowing part of me, on the other hand, was not. It made perfect sense.

"There is something important here that I need to bring your attention to so things are totally clear. You have heard me discuss with Catherine in class the quantity of Guides she works with have you not?" she asked me. From my nod of confirmation she continued.

"Your energies and hers are very similar. Are you aware of the large *quantity* of Guides that work with you as well...?

And there it was.

I breathed a sigh of relief at the confirmation that brought me back away from the consideration of my own potential insanity. Though she had brought only the Angel and little girl to my attention, I now knew I had been accurate about the others.

"Do you understand that this is not normal? That most people have only two to four guides? This, when a teacher such as myself sees it, is a flag to go the distance in assisting the individual, because they are of importance and 'worth teaching.'"

She had not a drop of drama or ego involved in the information she was delivering, simply proceeded with the reading.

"The other important point that must be made here is with regard to a misconception many people have about Angels. They believe that each person has their very own guardian angel at their side, when in truth they are simply picking up the energies of a *Guide*. The Angelic realm serves all of creation, and I'm not saying these people have not experienced an interaction, but it's not normal either to have an entity of this kind walking at your side as a *primary* Guide as you do. This beings energy is much higher and finer, and you have the rare ability to hold and be that finer energy level as well. Do you understand? ...You *have* actually seen her you know..."

She made the last sentence a statement.

In a heart beat I knew exactly the moment she spoke of, when once in the middle of the night there had been a beautiful bright being in my room. I had dismissed it at the time but noted that car headlights couldn't possibly be reflecting off of a mirror…since there *was* no mirror in my bedroom and no parking lot or road nearby. It was interesting to see so many incidents in my life starting to make sense.

She proceeded at that point to pass additional messages on from my guides and even some relatives on subjects of income generation, getting a job, lowering my expenses. I'd have to say that particular section of the discussion weighed heavily on me. I was exhausted. Tired of trying to live this life in its mundane aspects and obviously failing. I suppose I was so aware of the urgency for humanity and my path that it proved an overwhelming combination to mentally process.

I appreciated learning the name of the little girl spirit, and being apologized to for so many years of this life being direction-less. They also had a few other introductions that brought certain Guides to my conscious attention so I could better work with them and understand some of the signals and signs they use. At the bottom line was the declaration that I was on my divine path. Nice to hear through all of the scarier news and realizations.

I wanted to know the Angels name, but was told only that I know her well, and when the time is right for that to be revealed, many things about who I am would make sense to me. I was looking forward to that day. And honestly, a bit frightened of it as well.

Chapter Nine

Mediumship of the trance-dramatic nature had been but the first of the gifts I would have the ability to realize. Mental mediumship was next on the list. The class sat in the library in the usual circle and we were instructed to move into an altered state, link with a guide or "communicator" and deliver a message for someone else in the room. I was *very* uncomfortable with this, and had no idea how to even begin. A *communicator* is the term they use for the relative of a person who has died, but wishes to communicate or assist in some way. If you have ever watched the television series with John Edwards called *Crossing Over*, then you have seen mental/platform mediumship in excellent demonstration.

I had no idea what to do, so I entered the exercise with a declaration to, as usual, be "open" to spirit. I may often seem casual in my language about these things, but in truth take it all very seriously, with a reverence that threatens to incapacitate me if I dwell on it too deeply. In this exercise, that reverence was to be shifted into a comedy club act for several minutes.

I had not closed my eyes for very long before, *clairvoyantly*, I saw clearly a very large green parrot pacing on the floor in front of me. I did my best to ignore it and call forth the person/spirit I was supposed to get a message from. I even went so far as to try and "shoo" the bird, explaining that I was trying to do this exercise and I needed him to go away! But this creature was very insistent, and I eventually gave up. In exasperation I asked, "So, are you the communicator? Do you have a message for someone?

The bird's insistence turned to excitement as he instantly turned and flew across the room to land on the head of the first of my classmates on the left side of the circle. My mumbling to myself internally intensified.

"Fantastic.....I'm supposed to talk to a person and I'm getting a bird. I must be totally doing this wrong.....

This made the following class discussion quite uncomfortable for me, but I knew better than to NOT share exactly what I was getting. When asked, I queried whether or not Barbara (the classmate that this bird seemed to be interested in), had ever had such a pet. When she said no I felt my stomach sink, but our tutor lead me through what was happening in her usual wonderful way.

I can not stress how fantastic it is to sit with a teacher who can "see" everything happening in a room. For the purposes of learning how to develop these types of abilities, I don't know how in the world it could be believed or managed without that type of support.

"What color is the bird?" she asked me, and I replied that it was green with red cheeks. The next parts of the message delivery taught me how the use of symbol, the meaning known to either the medium or client is used to translate a message. This bird, apparently, is very real and accompanies one of my "regular" guides. To me, the color green symbolizes healing; red is for action, and parrot carries the energies of communication. To my amazement, once thoroughly translated, it made perfect sense to Barbara. It was accompanied by a further message that I explained as I had "heard" it.

I was fascinated, but not really impressed. The demonstration was shaky at best, but I appreciated it seemed to have meaning. Not to mention my relief that I wasn't just seeing random birds like a crazy person.

From there we moved on to others in the room bringing through messages. I was so engrossed in self analysis that it took me by surprise when Catherine spoke up that she believed the message she was receiving was for me. She began describing a woman who could only have been my maternal grandmother. The physical description brought up such detail in life history, body and mannerisms it was incredible. I was so honored by the appearance. Grandma had passed over not even a year prior, and at 90+ years of age, it had not been an easy exit for her. It was about the difficulties, lack of physical glamour and courage that she came to speak to me about. She reminded me again, as she had done so many times in her life that I was "strong like her" and needed to remember that.

I thanked her and Catherine only to be quickly transitioned to Sarah who apparently had also had my very emphatic grandmother insisting on a "part 2" to the message given to her granddaughter. How could I not laugh? Her personality in spirit was as demanding as it had been in life, and I couldn't have been more grateful. As time begins to wash away the certainties of memories from this experience, nothing could explain a woman from England and another from Switzerland knowing such immense detail about me or Grandma. In truth, Grandma harkened in a reality to Stansted that nothing else could have.....and she was far from finished in this first exercise. According to Catherine, she had marched into the room on the first day, declared to Catherine "we'll be speaking later," and stood off to the side for several days until the opportunity arose to communicate with her granddaughter. Anyone that has ever met her would tell you that this was *classic* grandma.

The second exercise later that afternoon would be one of the most fantastic for me in learning my mental mediumship abilities. A continuation of the first, but in one-on-one format, I was teamed with Catherine. This pleased me not only because we seemed to have a natural affinity for each other, but because our Tutor had pointed out that she works with a large quantity of Guides as well. It seemed like the perfect opportunity, among many.

Our instructions were to "link" again with a "communicator" and pass a message specifically to our partner. Again I was very intimidated and nervous. I closed my eyes to "see" what I could see, and just started talking about whatever came to me. After a few moments, with a smile on her face, Catherine stopped me.

"Wow, that was *excellent*...but let me help you understand what you were just doing." She asked me at that moment were I felt the energy, and I replied honestly that it was in my solar plexus.

"Does it feel heavy or light?" She guided.

"Heavy."

"That's correct. And what a good experience this is. What you are doing is reading me *psychically*. And doing a very fine job of it! But let's move your energy "higher" so that you can link."

I followed her guidance and felt the energies move out of my solar plexus and up through my body and beyond. It's fascinating and wonderful to have a concrete knowledge in working with these interactions. So I again put forth the inquiry to see if there was a "communicator" that would like to speak to Catherine.

Almost immediately I could see (clairvoyantly with my eyes closed), a woman in a pink dress to my left. I told Catherine what I saw, though not even remotely certain I wasn't making it up. After describing her, my partner said she believed she knew who it was.

"Please ask her what her profession was."

I froze and started to panic.

You want me to have a conversation with a figment of my imagination!?

But when I turned back to the woman, the scene had changed and, as if in answer to the question, the woman had moved to stand in front of a blackboard with a pointer in hand. I relayed this to Catherine and ended my information with a guess.

"I think she was a teacher."

Catherine lit up at the information which was apparently a confirmation as to the identity of the woman. Next she asked an even more challenging question.

"Please ask her if she married him."

Yikes.

I turned back, however, to find the woman was showing me her hand. On her finger was a diamond engagement ring. But as I looked it vanished, only to reappear and disappear several more times. I translated this to Catherine and suddenly realized I could hear the woman speaking in my head.

"He wasn't the right one."

All of this and more made sense to Catherine as the conversation continued onward and the rest of the personal message was passed along in a succession of words and pictures.

Had I not been sitting with an experienced medium herself, this training exercise would not have been so monumentally solidifying for me. At the next juncture of the conversation, Catherine was able to point out that I had shifted into a discussion and relay with one of her guides, and that I was no longer talking to the woman in the pink dress. This too was an excellent experience because the "feel" of the energies was totally different. If I had to best describe it at the time I would say that speaking with a Guide is "higher" in feel than speaking to a Communicator.

Placement was to be observed as another factor for me. Certain entities seemed to consistently communicate with me from one side or the other. This helped me to identify them even further.

It should be mentioned that for any medium there is a "fight or flight" natural mechanism built-in that can engage quite automatically. When in an altered state, our primary "gatekeeper" naturally protects us, but on first approach, any spirit that we are unfamiliar with can spook a medium on "energetic impact." To lessen these effects and maintain the safest perimeter, many mediums will not speak directly with any entity other than their own guides, whom they enlist as translators. This is especially true for trance mediums. Allowing access to themselves for any passing entity would be foolish and uncomfortable.

There seemed, for me, to be a balance starting to build in who spoke to me, when and how. In any interaction, if I felt unsure or needed a respectful emissary, I would simply call out to one of my guides on the internal planes and ask for assistance. And thankfully, assistance was always fully present. They all seemed to have patience and know how to manage things on my behalf even when I consciously didn't have a clue as to what was transpiring.

In my personal message session which followed the translation I gave to Catherine, I had the honor of meeting my Uncle. This gentle man, son to my persistent maternal grandmother who had come through two other mediums today, had passed before I was even born. The conversation was absolutely fascinating coming through such an excellent medium, and as undeniable as Grandma had been in factual confirmation. This Uncle knew so much about me, the things in my house and behaviors that could never be guessed at with such accuracy. He came forth with project guidance as well as frustration in my belief that I am alone. I had often stood in rooms by myself and mourned a life that seemed full of solitude and unfinished projects. He came to guide, support, and banish forever the ridiculous notion that I "walk alone." And his sense of humor was as pronounced as his serious side. I would have to say that at the time I was both greatly honored and a bit confused as to why I have so much spirit assistance. I just kept thinking…

Don't they all have more important things they could be doing…?

Chapter Ten

After dinner that evening, and before the presentation of platform mediumship in the chapel, I wandered up to my room for the briefest of pauses in a crazy-busy day. I was really excited at the prospect of having the chance to see an open-to-the-public demonstration of multiple mediums that was scheduled for the evening ahead. It would be my first.

Laying back on the bed and staring up at the ceiling I allowed some of the experiences of the week to process. Seeing them from a slightly detached viewpoint I couldn't help but laugh out loud at the insanity of it as the rest of the world would see it.

"You guys have got to be kidding me, " I spoke aloud, as I had now become accustomed to doing with my guides and the virtual "troop" of entities that I was only now beginning to acknowledge were my constant companions. *"What am I supposed to tell my parents??"*

I rubbed my eyes and sarcastically, with amusement, launched into a pretend conversation that seemed ludicrous.

"Oh, hey mom & dad....I got to meet your brother who passed away, yeah, Grandma brought him to see me in England...."

I ended the conversation with a sound of frustration and followed it with a decision.

"No way. I'm just *not* going to share this. They won't get it or they won't believe me...and I'm tired of being the rouge child in the primary and extended versions of this family. Everyone thinks I'm nuts anyway."

Memories of my cousin declaring me to be in need of an intervention when the family first heard I was "into metaphysics" nearly 10 years ago came to mind. They told my mother I had obviously joined a cult. And this marked the demise of my comfortable extended "family" interactions. I was the declared black sheep, and nothing had ever been comfortable since. My parents had later followed suit, as their own metaphysical journey had tumbled into denial and anger in their unwillingness to deal with "their stuff" as I call it.

This process and journey of facing yourself can be hard. I have great compassion for those who at least try, and immense respect for those who are committed to pressing on and facing any personal issue or inner turmoil. At this moment, however, I did not see the point in displaying myself to my parents for ridicule and rejection....*again.*

The chapel was empty when I entered. I was nearly 30 minutes early so that I could get a front row seat for the proceedings. This was *my* week, and I didn't wish to miss a moment or an opportunity to learn and experience all that was available. To my astonishment or, actually, as seemed to be the norm, Grandma came through *again* to discuss this recent, specific decision with me. In a room filled with over 100 people hoping to get one of the few messages, Grandma was not to be deterred. And her message was simple:

"You think these people are being nice to you (family, parents), but they're not. You need to stand up for who you are!"

She concluded with a final endearment that was intensely personal, and unmistakable in its message.

I would have to, at this point, say *thank you Grandma.* And tell you (the reader) that I did "stand up."

Chapter Eleven

There were so many of these immense moments during the week that it would be impossible to include them all. The intension of my focus in this sharing of experiences is to keep a firm focus on the awakening itself. I hope that as you read this you are ever keeping in mind how I, as a person fairly "normal" in the view of the daily business community, found their way…discovered their gifts and truth.

Stansted Hall, for me was the answer to the greatest prayer in my life.

Dear God please show me who I am.

It was similar, I would imagine, to the children in the movie "X-men" being brought to *Xavier's School for the Gifted* and discovering they aren't crazy, or alone in their "mutant" gifts. Stansted Hall was my equivalent to "Mutant High (School)".

Besides the experiences I've already shared, there were quiet discussions with my Guides in the garden. Fascinating physical manifestations that could only be compared to watching science fiction… but without the fiction. In one classroom exercise a demonstration of physical transfiguration by spirit was initiated for all to see. In a totally darkened room the ectoplasm of a medium was drawn out of the body to create an "overshadowing" so that the Guide could present himself in full physical view of the audience. It was magnificent to watch a classmate seemingly transform from woman, to monk in full clothing, to Native American Indian before our eyes. And it did not take clairvoyance to see it. In another demonstration we added our energies together to assist a little girl spirit to make a table dance and walk across the room on its own! And in yet another, we witnessed full trance healing as a Guide worked through their Medium in a display of reiki like no other I could have imagined in the world.

Needless to say, I would not go home from Stansted Hall as the same person who arrived. The opportunity to work with the Guides and the immensity of discovering my own abilities would lead to a different life. Or would it? As I stepped into the final classroom session in the Library it was not without panic.

Knowing now that statements vocalized and help requested did not go unanswered in this place, I said a silent prayer that my Guides would not end my week without my knowing what to do next. Oh, sure, I was supposed to close down my consulting business, get a job and try not to feel guilty over my financial choices of the last three years, but what was I supposed to do with all this mediumship stuff? My primary prayer of *who am I* has become an even larger question in the possibly cataclysmic revealing of *what do I do with all of this*?!

A week of powerful energies and transforming experiences had left me both tired and wired. I was more at home here than I had ever felt anywhere, and going home was a daunting and depressing thought. As I soaked in the energies of the Library, and our Tutor started us off with the opportunity to ask questions, I considered whether to speak up about my fears. A reassuring nod from Catherine gave me the courage to ask for another trance session. I thought I was supposed to go home and be able to do this. But I had only managed to allow the Angel through that one time, and I didn't think I could do it again without the support of the group. Maybe if I accomplished it one more time without shaking apart…

No sooner had I asked the question when one of the strongest and most powerful waves of trance I had ever felt swept the room. Something was happening, but I stood my ground and waited for the teacher's instruction. She "checked-in" and smiled as she realized that the reason she had not been guided to set up a specific lesson plan for this class, was because she was going to be the medium for the guides to come through in full trance to speak to us one last time before we left. I could not have been more grateful.

As was their custom, the guides spoke to each of us in turn to assist and uplift, but they made it clear from the moment of arrival that this was for me.

My tears flowed freely as I released the fear and tension. When you think that Spirit can't surprise you with a giant realization, that's about the time they deliver another…or so the trend seems to be with me.

"We know you are extremely overwhelmed. There is so much to do, so many changes to make when you get home. We ask that you trust us and just take it one thing at a time. Do you remember that one single point of purpose that you can feel burning within you? The one that tells you that your life is incredibly important? Though you can not yet see that purpose in full form, we ask that you hold on to that knowingness with all your being. It is correct."

Spirit next revealed to me a frightening fact that consciously I was not entirely aware of. Or, to speak more accurately, I was not aware had "worked."

"You have tried to exit this life more than once. We are aware of this," they stated. *"It was prevented."*

I was shocked.

Though as I said, I had never attempted or considered suicide, they clarified that my intention to give up had initiated a chain of events to die on more than one occasion. This information was followed by a very strong pleading.

"We ask you please....please stay. Will you hold on?.... will you do this?"

Of course my answer was yes. Though I didn't know *how* I was going to do it...how do you stand amongst such beings of light and love and deny them a request...especially one so immense? Somehow, with their help, I hoped I would find a way to keep going.

Chapter Twelve

At the door to the library he was standing with an almost distressed look about him. Ryan had agreed to drive me back to London-Heathrow Airport to see me off, but he was a full class early in his timing.

"We have to leave *right now,*" he flatly stated, "and I don't know why."

His declaration fit right in with his new awareness's, and I can't help but smile looking back on it. One thing that becomes very clear to anyone working with their Guides and trusting their "intuition" is to *really* trust it. It takes practice and surrender, but as spirit and a person's higher self can see "the road ahead," their promptings and guidance is always important to follow.

So I said my goodbyes early and dashed out the front door behind him. I would say it was actually better that way, because another hour of goodbyes would have made leaving even more difficult. And saying goodbye to Ryan at the Airport was gut-retching enough.

As we lay together in each other's arms the night before he had been very aware of my sadness.

"I don't want you to feel bad about this." He had said in a rare moment of true softness. He was my British-Capricorn-tough-guy who definitely wasn't into displays of emotion. "It's better to have had this time than not, and that's what I want you to hold onto."

So for him, I was strong and didn't let him see the tears. But come they did after he had turned the corner at customs and was out of my sight.

From this point at customs, to the time the plane took off was as immense in its demonstration of Guide assistance as any experienced at Stansted Hall. And I'm immensely thankful for it to this day.

Keeping in mind that Ryan had been incredibly urgent about our earlier departure time, began to have reason as one delay after another seemed to keep me from the departure gate. I would have to say that both of us were incredibly shocked at the impact of the energies of the airport on top of everything else. It was like a switch inside of us had been turned on and the "volume" turned up. We could energetically feel the impact of the thoughts and feelings of every person in the airport...or at least that's the best way to describe it. I wanted to cover my ears to drown it out, but I was receiving it at every level, the primary having nothing to do with physical hearing! It was comforting to have Ryan to cling to, but I was soon on my own.

When I finally got to the departure gate I had only 20 minutes to spare before they closed the doors. To my shock, a very cold flight attendant greeted me and flatly stated that I would not be granted access to this flight due to the fact that I did not have a boarding pass. I blinked at her in shock and gazing down at my ticket pointed out to her the bold letters reading b-o-a-r-d-i-n-g p-a-s-s. But apparently this was the wrong *type,* and she said I would have to go all the way back to the front entrance of the airport and get the correct one.

Panic hit my chest hard. There was no physical way I could get there and back all the way through customs in time and not miss this flight. What would I do? I had no money for a hotel room or change-of-ticket. No way to reach Ryan. And the only thing the flight attendant said in answer to my question as to how I could make it in time was:

"Run."

And I did.

Not even knowing exactly where I was going and dragging my heavy bag behind me. As I ran, I internally screamed to my guides for assistance.

Please...please... help me make this flight. Don't leave me stranded in this airport. Don't let the plane leave without me. Don't let it leave the gate....

By some miracle I made the gate in 19 minutes. Customs didn't hold me up, and the ticket agent, seeing my obvious distress, gave me access to a reserved seat that I'm pretty sure she wasn't supposed to assign. By the time I got to the actual door to the plane I was sweating, breathing hard, and for the first time in my life unable to coherently even get to my seat. Never mind how I was going to lift my bag into the overhead compartment.

Another flight attendant led me to the seat when I asked for help and she was thankfully kind enough to stow my luggage.

I didn't care. I can't remember ever before being in distress as I was at that moment. I just sat there. Again I asked my guides for assistance in balancing. I think my lack of ability to deal with the situation was even more frightening that nearly missing the plane. What had become of me?

Their response to my request was instantaneous and physical. Though I never sleep easily on a plane, and certainly *not* after a 20 minute panicked run, I felt myself drifting. I understood their intention, as it's often easier to balance me in a sleep state. My last recollection was a curious announcement from the pilot that departure was no longer going to be on time due to a bizarre and sudden deployment of the back door emergency shoot.

I awoke an hour and a half later, and I felt better.

To my surprise we were, however, still at the gate. I drowsily picked up tidbits of conversation from complaining passengers that their televisions, overhead lights and radios were not functioning properly. Men in yellow engineering suits moved back and forth from the back door. Apparently the entire emergency chute mechanism had had to be replaced.

I couldn't have cared less.

I was feeling like I had just been slammed back to earth and wasn't especially capable of a coherent thought. We eventually took off, as the plane issues were resolved and I resigned myself to dealing with the missed connection in New York when that time arrived. I was not thrilled to discover that television and electronic equipment were pretty much out of the question, as they were now painful to my senses. Not that I could tell you *why* or which senses those *were* exactly. So I amused myself with listening to my CD player which didn't seem to bother me in small doses.

At some point about two hours into the seven hour transatlantic flight, I got a clairvoyant image of two index fingers being brought together. The flashover was accompanied by a very clear message which stated:

The two are connected.

This snapped me to attention. What two things are connected? The message was gently repeated.

And the answer hit me like a ton of bricks.

No WAY.

I was actually angry in my insistence that what was being communicated to me *must* be wrong… *had* to be wrong.

And for the next half hour…or more…I flatly refused to believe it or discuss it.

What they were bringing to my attention was that my direct request for divine intervention, to *stop the plane from leaving the gate*, had been the reason for multiple non-vital system failures. I had had an emergency, and the emergency chute had deployed.

This was an overwhelming declaration to me. Inherent within the implications included not only physical manifestation of my powerful assistance and abilities, but a responsibility too immense to imagine.

"You can't tell me the plane "blew up" because I got upset." Was all I could manage to whisper to my Guides.

I sat in shock for awhile and finally gave them my childish double-dog-dare-you demand to give me a sign *right now* that this was true.

And I waited.

Not three minutes later my confirmation arrived. I glanced beside me at another passenger's television screen, the volume coming through the earphones just enough to remind me of the meaning behind the movie scene playing.

The movie was (of course) the *X-men*. And the scene playing was from the beginning of the second movie when Jean Gray has a misbalance of her telepathic and energetic powers. This misbalance is caused by a moment of upset that momentarily causes a malfunction of all electrical systems in the science center.

O.K., so I got the point.

But I have to tell you that it would be weeks before I would fully accept it.

So I slept, ate and just tried to stay as coherently grounded as possible. Later into that same flight home, I had to laugh at my shocked response to my clairvoyance showing me an interaction between the lady sitting next to me and *her* guide assistance. This woman was a particularly dramatic and difficult passenger. Her foot in a cast she displayed a nearly constant string of drama for attention. Anything the flight attendant asked her to do she refused.

Coming out of sleep near the end of the flight I was shocked to "see" a tiny deer standing in front of the woman, licking her hands as she slept. I clearly heard my guides say.

She is teaching this woman gentleness.

Boy, had life changed.

The 7-Year Countdown to 2012

The 7-Year Countdown to 2012

The Anatomy of a Test

I had been told by my Guides that it would take nearly three months of serious rest to recuperate from the last three years in addition to my time in England. And they weren't wrong. But I noticed regular and powerful assistance at times when I wasn't my usual mentally-quick self. And boy was *that* an understatement. My friends reported at both Stansted Hall and upon my return to the United States that I was kind-of amusing in my randomness during conversations, and displayed a general inability to remember everything that occurred. I found it anything *but* amusing, since I had been charged with totally changing my career and dealing with a life I honestly had no interest in returning to anyway. And total rest wasn't entirely on the three-month agenda.

We were entering a period during 2001-2002/3 I call "the year of the hurricanes." It actually started in Virginia for me, and then seemed to follow me back to Florida as life progressed. Perhaps as part of the overall plan, if there truly was one at play, the Virginia storm brought a gift. I was reeling from the impact of having my abilities suddenly 'switched on,' and could barely function. I did little driving and a lot of just trying to survive for a few weeks when I returned from England. I was shocked by the insanity of it at times, as I had to actually unplug the television set from the wall because it was too loud even when it was *turned off*. Electronics and their hum were unbearable, and when I prayed for relief, I got it in an unexpected complete east-coast-of-Virginia blackout for 5 days following the storm landfall. Despite the annoying heat and humidity that prevailed without air conditioning, it was such a relief. And more than a little wild to consider that I could reach out and *feel* across half a state like that.

So as my balance returned a bit, I initiated the necessary relocation. In just 7 days time I went from decision to landing in my new home in Florida and left the state of Virginia behind. It felt like a run-to-the-finish line with an unseen timeline pushing me forward. I understood it by feel, (as feeling was now one of my leading, acknowledged senses), and I stood staring up at the sky. Within a few hours of the moving truck depositing me at my new residence and pulling away, I took a deep breath and watched the 2001 Harmonic Convergence align. Perhaps that was the point of the timing.

For the next several months some large scale synchronicities would appear on my path. One of the other 12 students I had attended the library class with at Stansted in England turned out to live within 40 minutes of my new home. She and I had not actually spoken directly more than once while I was in training, and I couldn't help but think, "Jeez...what are the chances that she actually lives nearby?"

The second supporting point came when an announcement was made that several of the primary instructors from Stansted were now going to come regularly and teach in my new city of residence. Again, what are the chances of that...? So I settled in with new roommates - two guys - and wasn't *that* going to be another new experience for me. One was a dear friend, and the other a music teacher. I appreciated the companionship, male energy and feeling of safety it brought though, as I worried how I was going to support myself next. And this brings us to "the test."

As if I needed another challenge, I was told that I was about to face a soul-level test. For anyone living under the misconception that life gets easier and everything is solved when you "arrive" on the platform of having great abilities, I can tell you that it does not. Being given more tools and knowledge just seems to mean that the opportunities get bigger for soul growth.

My work with altered state was progressing in private time with my new friend from Stansted, and this was where "the test" notification was revealed with no additional details about it. I would be told later (about a year or so down the road), that I had passed. And quite a test it was. Subtle, and requiring a true awareness of self-intentions. After a long and unsettling four months of trying to find a job and pick a career path, I was offered two jobs on the same day. One was working for a national, well respected nonprofit using all my current corporate skills and talents. It included an assistant, benefits, fun work, nice office environment and good salary. It was service-to-society wrapped up in bow.

The second job offer was in a totally new field that would require training from the ground up, unpredictable difficult work, endless on-call hours and the pay was $10,000 less with barely the assurance that the salary level would actually pay my basic bills. This second job offer was in child protective services, and I felt the more massive "pull-to-service" it was bringing with it. Along with a certainty that now ruled my life. I must continue to make choices based on trusting my intuition and connection to my guides above all else…even when the outward appearances or intellectual reasons made something seem like the wrong choice.

So I meditated. And spoke with my friends and family. It was pretty much unanimous…and violently so if you spoke to my parents…that taking the child protective services job was unacceptable. Not enough money and a ridiculous career choice to start over rather than use my hard-earned excellent corporate skills. But I knew what I had to do. My training was taking me into "the dark places," and as a warrior I understood that I didn't come into this incarnation to participate in just the "fluffy" situations. So the game was on and for twelve months I would be on-call twenty-four hours a day, seven days a week through the "year of the hurricanes" as four devastating storms crossed over the state wreaking havoc and forcing transitions in every area.

This was also the year that Florida "privatized" the child protective service system. My brother had once called me *Christiane Amanpour…the Angel of Death.* (And I'm still a bit torn about whether that's a fair designation.) He said he noticed that whenever I appear in someone's life they are about to get handed the absolute truth and soul-level opportunity to transition in some way. They will be forced to face themselves and leave behind that which does not serve their highest path. Ok…that was the PC way to say it….what he *actually* said, was that when I show up it's because someone's world is about to blow up and they are going to get their ass handed to them if they don't consciously recognize the change they need to make themselves.

Great.

But I've noticed that he doesn't appear to be wrong about that.

Not that it's a really fun position to be in, since most people just get pissed and refused to deal with their issues. And let me just confirm if you were wondering....*yes*...the messenger really does get shot.

Frequently.

So there I stood, with more than 25 children in varying states of trauma in my care; hurricanes destroying houses and lives (in a necessary tear down and wake-up call, I do realize), and me walking a plan to uplift the system into the new private-care corporate offices taking over the state of Florida protective services counseling. They didn't know me, but they loved the program I created...for about five minutes. Until the first hurricane hit and everyone decided that making a profit was more important than saving children.

Christiane Amanpour.

They had been given a choice and a chance to uplift the system, and instead they actually choose the money. Even going so far as to *remove* services as vital as psychiatric and psychological care from abused children to do it. And by the end of that horrible year, I knew it was time to leave. I had made a serious difference in the lives of some of the individual children and families in my care, though. Saved three children, ages 1, 3 and 10 who had been raped and beaten by their father. Built a case to end his paternity and found all of them loving adoptive homes despite their critically bad behaviors. Got a violent, mentally unbalanced 16 year old reunited with his grandparents and out of the corrections system where he didn't belong. All in all I can see the positive reasons and opportunities inherent in the adventure. I used my new abilities as much as possible. But within two months of my exit from child protective services, I would discover that the learning curve had cost me my health.

In the Light of the Shaman

Before I leap to the next segment of the journey, there is an important exploration into my newly discovered abilities that is important to reveal. One of the main points of metaphysical practice and ability that is key in this time period for all souls is that a single-element modality is limiting to the soul. The children of this age are born with many abilities that are likened to a "toolbox" and meant to be merged and used nearly all at the same time or in a mix as each situation requires. Being 'just a medium' or studying only one method of practice is akin to getting stuck in an unnecessary rut. The universe is unlimited, and so are we. So naturally my multi-layered abilities were each coming on line and revealing themselves to prove that point.

One sunny weekend afternoon, shortly after I had started the job in child protective services, I made a declaration to my guides that I was *done* with all the serious-life-stuff and taking a well deserved break. I went digging into my storage boxes for a mindless romance novel I remembered purchasing a while back, with a serious determination to relax. I look back on this moment now as the comedy strip it must have been from spirit's point of view.

The book storyline was set in the South American jungles, and if you remember, on that crazy night in England it had been revealed to me that I 'walk' with a very large black jaguar spirit guide. She is my protector, and I had been told that this shape-shifter and I actually merge. Now that's all well and good, but I honestly didn't understand either the mechanics or purpose of it.

And wasn't *that* all about to change.

I didn't even get past the prologue of the novel before discovering that hidden within the storyline was an instruction manual and outline of a healer/woman/shape shifter who works with the Black Jaguar Clan. A shaman. And a complete discussion about how they work together, why, what the difference is between the black and spotted jaguar clans, and oh so much more.

In a romance novel.
Really?
So much for playtime and relaxation.

Needless to say, it lead me down a magical but serious path that merged and assisted me in understanding my placement in child protective services for the time I was there. But it actually did a lot more than that in the end. I went in search of the author. She obviously wasn't a romance novelist first and shaman second, and I had some interesting discussions and meetings with other practicing shamans through that relationship. Learning about this modality of metaphysical ability and practice brought me measurably closer with my own jaguar guide, and I'm grateful for the cat's assistance and protection in the healing work I did with many of the children.

One night however, by email, I was shocked at a letter I received from this primary shaman and international best-selling author. I had been considering going and taking a class from her since I really appreciated these new gifts, and wanted to allow my abilities to expand further. Working in the realm of altered state is serious business, and when a shaman journeys for you, it is often a warrior's walk when soul recovery and extraction are involved. To briefly explain, traumatic experiences and encounters with others can lead to pieces of the soul/your energy being taken, lost or connected to inappropriately. This, of course, is the human mental concept for describing it, as it all wraps around energy, decisions, etc. But at the bottom line, a shaman and his guides will work with yours to 'face-off' against, remove or recover whatever is lost or out of place. This being said, I work as a healer, and this sort of interaction is understood and natural to me at the warrior level.

So as my discussions got deeper with her, I happened to mention my mediumship. This was met with instant and furious disapproval. I believe her exact words were:

"You need to stop interacting with that mediumship stuff. Anyone who walks with a black jaguar and has your shamanic abilities is not meant to be working with mediumship."

And wasn't *that* just the most ridiculous thing I had ever heard. It was right up there with the Spiritualist National Union's declaration that reincarnation is a falsehood; and several British-style mediums declaration that seeing guides (vs. relatives that have passed) away isn't the definition of mediumship.

I just sat there and blinked at the computer screen for a few moments. It wouldn't be the first time that someone making an attempt at control would tell me to stop talking to my guides or that they weren't actually there.

I was getting the message loud and clear. Dogma, ego, territorialism and fear had some of what could be considered the highest-functioning metaphysical instructors in the world completely stuck in their own particular 'ruts.'

Needless to say, I kindly thanked her and moved on. My guides had said I was not to train with her and some of the others because it would hinder my growth. I was beginning to see why. So I simply blessed them their way, and silently thanked them for the unintended lesson they delivered.

This gave me the best of both worlds. I advanced the use of my abilities and understanding, but also understood why relying on the guidance coming *through* me would always be the higher path. If I could stay clear enough and centered enough to keep it as the focal point in spite of the challenges raging around me on the earth plane.

Agreeing to Free Them

My next career position on the path would lead me to international waters….literally. But I would face first a monumental health crisis. The year of the hurricanes and walk through the world of child protective services took a heavy toll. It was an impossible job for a human, and for me, with amplified sensitivity and empathic abilities, it was devastating. I fought the good fight, but didn't realize that I had taken the pain from every child I carried in my arms. At best, an experienced empath and healer would have aimed at proper grounding and release, but I was a junior avenger and couldn't have predicted the overload would land me in the hospital in surgery for growths in my abdomen.

Of course.

A situation and incident I would spend nearly a year struggling to get back from, and nearly not choose to stay.

People don't realize that *sensitive* means *sensitive*. Period. You don't get to turn it off, and it may bring you to moments in the lifetime when you can't imagine how you'll go on. I can tell you now, that I will *never* allow another surgery. And that is on an equal self-protection chain-of-decisions with who I allow in my space…medically, professionally and personally. Not an easy journey; but there would be a new set of support mechanisms, and even a full-blown intervention to stop me from releasing the physical plane this time around.

And quite an intervention and next step in revealing my abilities it would turn out to be.

Battles in Child Protective Services and dodging hurricanes weren't the only large projects going on during this period. I was training. Hard. And we're not talking about attending those love-me-hug-me-fuzzy-bunny types of metaphysical classes either. In power groups I worked in altered state along a primary path that was flanked by private-time interactions with spirit. I had shifted from years of just reading about it all, to the necessary experiential phase… and boy was it a ride. I few times a year I was supported by the framework of the classroom or private sessions, but always followed the lead of my own guides for exercises and participation. I didn't even *ask* what the title of the class was, just stepped up to the plate and knew that spirit would use that framework to advance and work with me at a deeply personal level.

One of these classes, if spirit had told us the true purpose in advance or the outcome, I'm certain most of us would have declined to participate in. A small group of very advanced practitioners stepped into a workshop called "Healing the Generations." I was nearing the end of my child protective services timeline and was already exhausted from battle. For others in the room I noticed the exercises in altered state were bringing them to crisis points as well as healing points by surfacing childhood abuse issues and other traumas. (Like I didn't get enough of that at work…right?) But for me, as I've grown accustomed to, I work in so many dimensions that only pieces of what transpires are given to me consciously at the time of spirit interaction. And this is appropriate to keep my personality as balanced as possible. I can tell you that in one monumental exercise I was honored to stand before the generations, family and others I am associated with who are now in spirit. I have always had awareness of the sheer number, but it was immense to see them in person stretched out in a corridor in front of me…hundreds of *thousands* of souls.

I remember the instructor guiding us to ask them what they needed from us, among other things. I was told that in the coming months my job was only to take care of myself. What I wasn't told until much later was that I had agreed at the soul level, during that interaction, that I would 'take on' and ground all of the energy/history/karma that was left within my soul group so that they would be free. Once and for all. And as the masses in my abdomen grew, and the doctor put off my surgery for four additional months; they brought me right up to the edge of death to complete the agreement.

Divine Intervention

I was standing in a new corporate position at the time I actually had the surgery. And as usual, spirit had prepared the support structure with an understanding boss and group who would let me work from home and give me paid recovery time. I appreciated that level of support from a survival point of view, but felt truly let down in the 'protection department' as well as the 'intuition department.' How could this be allowed to happen? Through my work in Child Protective Services I had fought for the children, and it seemed that my reward was more physical pain than anyone could bear. My belief in myself and spirit was shaken if not nearly completely broken. And they knew it.

I returned to work in a few weeks and soldiered on with daily pointless paperwork and a body that wasn't healing. Which was a natural succession of events since my mental and emotional devastation was pretty much blocking it. So what to do?

At about the 7-months-after-surgery marker I was reaching for a diet plan to curb the misery of the weight gain that had accompanied my inability to do anything but lay on the couch. I was also trying to remember the last time I actually had a happy moment. Months had stretched into years of pain, battle and survival. And I finally decided the last happy moment had been in England…in the library…with my guides. I might have still been angry with them for the events that had ensued, but there was nothing else left standing in my life actually worth living for at that point. So I did the only thing I could. I aimed at going back.

After the overload I had experienced on my last trip to train in England, it was no wonder that I wasn't getting on a plane without figuring out how to support myself a bit better. But with limited financial resources, I wondered what the best way to do that actually was. I figured I needed a 'babysitter' to handle logistics and make sure I didn't step off a sidewalk in front of a bus. On a regular basis for me, working in altered state for a couple of hours makes it tough to focus and function physically;

forget about trying to negotiate international travel and crowds during a whole week of this kind of 'deep sea diving.' And I was more fragile since the surgery; more sensitive with the advancing of my abilities.

In my consideration and attention to the possibilities, Spirit took the opportunity to bring about a few solutions that I now look back on as nothing short of a divine intervention. More important than actually achieving a return to England was to address my devastation. As I said, I wasn't healing. I didn't have a reason to. I was close to initiating events to exit the lifetime. And apparently they were going to bring in the big guns to stop it.

His name was Daniel.

I had once said it would take a Navy Seal to be my mate. A man as skilled and focused physically, as I was non-physically. I had even been reading books that included stories of the Teams. Not that I believe any given profession guarantees a good person, but it gave me a balance of masculine energy in a world I faced daily that sorely lacked it.

One afternoon I was talking to our current corporate security guy Shane, (my warrior soul naturally gravitating in friendship in that direction), and discovered that he and his actual team were all ex-Rangers, Navy Seals, Naval Intelligence, etc.

Hmmm.

What are the chances of *that*?

No rent-a-cops here.

And this brought me to a new realization. These guys specialized in close personal/bodyguard protection. You could hire them for something as simple as say *professional escort to handle the logistics for international travel to alleviate stress.* Apparently not an option reserved only for movie stars and diplomats.

And now I was beyond fascinated, while equally freaked out.

If I put together a profile as requested for a private escort to England, I was going to have to reveal why I needed it. And that meant opening myself up to massive ridicule and disbelief...and *way* too close to my workplace environment.

But I did it anyway....carefully.

I had had Shane sign a non-disclosure agreement and paid him outside of work for a consultation. He immediately aimed me at his team leader from another outside company and agreed to set up a second meeting.

But I was shaking. I didn't think I could sit through another reveal-your-weirdness session and allow myself to be that vulnerable again. Not that Shane had been judgmental in any way. He simply seemed client-focused and willing to accept the mission. But I still wasn't sure about going through it with a stranger.

Until Daniel walked in.

Aside from being incredibly good-looking, he had a calming manner similar to the energy a paramedic or first responder has in helping you feel balanced while ushering you past your panic. So I explained the situation without pulling any punches. International high-level psychic training. Get me there and back. Concerned about the sleepwalking thing on top of everything else. Looking for a solid energy anchor to ease the impact.

He took it well.

Was actually completely fascinated by it.

Which is the right energetic reaction I needed if I was going to pull it off, because resistance based on religious bias or any other issue wouldn't allow me to function.

And so we started the parade of email conversations to aim at the trip when I was financially ready. A relationship that would reveal itself to be for alternate reasons than travel.

Happy Halloween

As usual, it's necessary to shift back a bit in the story to paint a picture of a second string of events that occurred prior to the entrance of "the security boys." In the midst of corporate and healing challenges, I was, still attending metaphysical sessions and classes. I was also, as mentioned, reading novels about Navy Seals, the "Teams" and other things to try to find some sort of "happy place" as well as support in between the difficult life-stuff. My childhood ability to slip into altered state and "be" with a more supportive cast-of-characters hadn't abandoned me, and I used it now to hang on.

On one particular evening that also happened to be Halloween, I had a strange occurrence. Halloween had always been my favorite holiday. Even when I was little it had felt strangely important. I loved the autumn leaves, magic and nighttime moon. I wasn't a fan of getting dressed up or having to run around the block and interact with people, but the candy was a bonus. Instinctively I now realize I had always known that the veil between the spirit world and physical plane was thinner on this one night, and it made me excited as few things do. Like a gateway opening to touch *home* and a chance to be with my real family.

On this particular Halloween I found myself face-to-face with a man standing in the middle of my living room. A seriously *hot* looking man. His name was Michael. And to make things more twilight zone, he appeared to be the same character from the book I was sitting there reading, yet carried a heightened and very personal energy in relation to mine. It didn't feel anything close to imagination, and we had a lovely evening together.
Happy Halloween.

Now, I'm not unfamiliar with the concept of Lifemates. To me, it's a very important one. The public uses the term 'soul mates' to describe the ideal man or woman mate they are hoping to find and marry. I find that terminology to be annoyingly overused, and I put most romantic relationships into the category of 'educational program.' Some include love and fun mixed into deconstruction of the inauthentic self. These relationships frequently end badly when personalities resist the aforementioned educational program and start blaming each other, etc.

While I do appear to have a bit of a negative view of relationships, I have an unwavering belief in the existence and importance of what I call *Lifemates*. This I define as a great love between two souls that is truly supportive of whatever events and process are taking place. Lots of lifetimes and lots of relationships so yes, there is more than one lifemate that carries the energy of that level of soul connection. Though it is a *way* more refined and rare paring than the public's current version of "soul mate." This may be added to the amplified connection of being in the same primary soul group, and then you have an even more powerful love and partnership.

Experiencing relationships on the 'other side' as clearly as I experience those in normal physical plane existence has always been part of my skill set. And for the most part, I would say that it has saved both my life and my sanity more than once. But it was a very private matter for me. I shared it with no one and relegated it to "imagination" for most of my life. But my guides, and this Happy-Halloween guy in particular, were not going to allow my dismissal-to-imagination to continue. He 'walked with me' more regularly after that night. And the companionship was nice. Protective energy, hot guy....what's not to like?

At a private session a month or so later with an international British medium, our discussion turned to the complaint every single woman in the world has...when was I going to get to meet a great guy and aim at a stable relationship?

Her reply was somewhere between shocking, embarrassing and comical.

It took her a minute or two in private side conversation with the guides before she dropped the bomb on me.

"You know, you already *are* in a relationship. He's standing right there behind you," she said pointing directly at where I was aware that Michael was standing.

"You can SEE him?!" I asked incredulously.

"Of course," she answered, and proceeded to perfectly describe him.

Jeez.

"So he's real." I made it more of a statement than a question.

"Of course."

And my two worlds suddenly collided and made sense. Pushing me in the direction, for the first time, to consider the possibility of what having a lifemate on the *other* side of the veil would be like.

Enter the Lifemate

As my relationship grew professionally with Daniel-the-Bodyguard via email, I did something I had never done before. I decided to let him read the private notes about my first journey to England. It seemed to be a logical step. If I was going to throw a non-metaphysical person into a highly metaphysical environment, he was going to have to know how to actually protect and support me. But I was more than a bit skittish about this. Revealing myself and being vulnerable with a strange guy was not on my list of normally acceptable options. And it's important to know a few additional things about Daniel.

He was married with two small children, for starters. So I was taking care on other levels to protect myself. There would be no fooling around with a married guy and the ensuing karma and dishonor that type of behavior would bring. I had enough experience to also know that unbalanced, insecure wives can be nuts. I wasn't interested in becoming embroiled in their 'educational program." But after he had read the transcript and appeared to be in the right energetic, supportive state, I considered what the next step should be.

I agreed to a meeting. And despite my intentions to remain detached, I got more than I bargained for. His charisma in a room would be tough for any female to overlook, and after having a lengthy discussion about how his job would be a combination of physical security, logistics and energy awareness, I was surprised by the 'push' from my guides to actually hold his hand and read him for a moment.

First, let me just say, I *don't* usually read this way. Touching someone can lead to nausea and overload, so no thanks. But I had his permission as well as his curiosity in tandem with the push from spirit; though I wasn't too enthusiastic about the pressure or what might happen.

He had told me that his background was ex-Naval Intelligence, and in his current security business he was partnered with Mark, an ex-Navy Seal. The two of them had gone through BUDS together as swim buddies for this Navy Seal qualifications program. Beyond providing him with a bit of private information about his business and partnership, it seemed the main purpose of the event was for me to allow an energy merger. It was also revealed that he was, indeed, of my soul group. Only the second person I had met who could claim that 'family' position. This was a very big deal to me. Not that I knew exactly what to *do* with the information, but I'm sure the ensuing debate with my invisible guides was fascinating for him to witness, to say the least. *Welcome to my world buddy.* Regardless of my conscious intentions, I noticed that I seemed, again, to be on a train toward an unknown destination. And that train was about to pick up speed.

In between the personal and metaphysical drama, the corporation I was working for was also undergoing a massive and fast growth period. It turned out that even as I aimed at the possibility of traveling with Daniel for personal-metaphysical reasons, he and his partner Mark were in negotiations to take over all of international corporate security for the company. Not the separation of church and state I had hoped for, but there were larger forces at work.

I was starting to heal.

I was working a fast-paced job of marketing, event planning, public relations and corporate communications, yet somehow the energetics between Daniel and I were speeding my healing and taking my intuitive abilities to the next level. As I had been willing to jump off the diving board at age four for Pat-the-swimming-instructor, I was now willing to consider my abilities for use outside the metaphysical classroom where Daniel and the security boys were concerned. And our 'connection' was anything but normal.

I read for him and helped him realize the true purpose behind some major life-occurrences. His grandfather was also dying, and I was honored when he came to me the day following his death to talk to me about his grandson, and ask me to pass a message. This was a true "evidentiary" moment for Daniel. The message passed from his grandfather proved to him my abilities were accurate and lead to other discussions. To my surprise, I was told that Daniel's grandfather was also 'of my soul group.' This made three, and it wouldn't be the last time I would speak with this grandfather. A man I would eventually come to think of as my own.

In all my life, from a physical point-of-view, I had never felt the power and energy of a Lifemate incarnated. Sure I had dated, had a few relationships/educational programs, and even a near-miss with marriage. But they were for *certain*, not lifemate material. Daniel on the other hand, was. And wasn't that an annoying and complicated web. Married or not, every part of my energetics and body reacted to him. 90% of our interactions were by email vs. in person, but it didn't matter. We weren't dishonoring anyone, but we were certainly reuniting and having an emotional affair as time progressed. How could we not? Regardless of any other relationship he might have in any corner of his life, he and I just *were*. Soul group plus past-life Lifemate connection is like dropping an atom bomb in the middle of a room. When he would sit in the middle of the night and write me an email, his energy alone, reaching for me, was enough to wake me up at 1:00am. Anywhere he was, if he thought about me, we connected and I knew it. If he was struggling or tired, I had complete awareness of it. When he would travel out of state, I felt something I could only describe as 'an empty spot' geographically and knew immediately that he was no longer in the immediate area. I was keeping my balance as best I could, but such a 'pull' can push you to the point of insanity. And to make things more intense, his team *did* become the internal security group managing the corporations.

My job and his were on an intercept course…but for what purpose?

I can see now that he was sent in to pull me back from the edge and out of a life-devastation point. Be careful what you wish for right? I had said *it would take a Navy Seal.* And there he stood.

But I needed some explanation and balance about this. The whole experience unleashed a torrent of emotions.

It's him.

He's back.

How annoying to have such incredible knowingness without the details.

At one point, in a Starbucks, we had met for a quick cup of coffee. I hugged him hello, and as I was withdrawing, I suddenly flew back into his arms and heard myself saying "*I missed you.*" I held on for a minute like my life depended on it. He responded gently and with an understanding that neither of us could put our finger on. On the way out the door after our meeting was finished, he actually kissed me. He felt the same confusing and intense connection.

Though on most days not consciously, it was evident that he felt the immensity of our soul link. I began spending as much time with him in dreamtime as in waking hours. It was an insanity of living two separate lives with the same person, and beyond anything I had experienced with anyone else. Daytime-Daniel didn't remember consciously all of the conversations I had had with Dreamtime-Daniel, so I would have to stop and think where I was standing and which one I was talking to so not to embarrass myself.

One day, it came to a turning point for him.

As the Public Relations pro for the companies, I deployed my corporate skills to help him build his security company portfolio of marketing materials. I attended a day-long internal training class for his team that turned into a last-minute client protection detail. It happened so fast that he really didn't have time to think about the possible outcome of allowing me to stand in the middle of it all.

At one point, he had to stop his guys from allowing me to role play as "the client" in a training exercise. Which was a good thing when I realized the protectee/client actually gets grabbed and thrown to the ground in the scenario. He knew he couldn't let the boys touch me like that. And alternately, in the classroom portion of training, he had to stop playing a video that showed agents getting killed in the street when they screwed up a protection detail. He saw me (and I'm sure felt me) recoil across the room, and felt bad that he hadn't considered the effect it would have on me to be shown the footage without warning.

If the training portion wasn't enough stress, a potentially dangerous crowd situation of 25,000 was next on the day's itinerary. And of course I didn't follow his instructions to stay in the car. I was, after all, capable of taking care of myself. I knew though, as I always did, the moment he spotted me in the crowd taking PR photographs. From his vantage point on the overlook and steps of the arena looking out over the thousands of people his energy found mine with absolute certainty. And maybe that moment was the point of this soul-level exercise. To get him to understand the depth of his connection to me.

I had trained him to protect me.

This plus the lifemate factor crashed in on him. He yelled at me later about unimportant things first, as people often do before reaching the all-important heart-centered point.

"You are <u>never</u> allowed to come on exercises or details again!...What if something had gone wrong...I couldn't have gotten to you through the crowd...it wasn't my job today...I would have had to stay with my client...I would have had to leave you behind!"

And there it was.

A mix of feelings, emotions and a situation that needed to be dealt with.

So I returned to a wonderful practitioner and Shaman I had met along the way, and asked her to 'journey' for me. She had conducted a very accurate and successful soul recovery and extraction session for me in the past. And without providing her with much information about the situation, I sent her and her guides into the night in search of answers.

The Next Levels of Revealing

We've discussed how soul recovery and extraction works, but I wasn't quite prepared to find out that the soul who was waiting to meet her on the other side was actually *Daniel*. Though I suppose it shouldn't have surprised me. He had epic abilities in astral projection and connecting where I was concerned. Plus he was of *my* soul group.

He had come to explain that the last time he and I were together was in medieval England, around 725 A.D. He had been my husband, but unfortunately died of a fever and left me alone to eventually die of terrible grief. He stood before my Shaman friend now and handed her six crystal tears. Pieces of my soul that the guides would re-integrate. *"Please return these to her. It is what she lost to grief."*

This and other items were handled, discussed and aligned with other guides and interactions during the same session. Mercifully, doing exactly what was necessary to assist me. It didn't sever the connection between Daniel and I, nor does it bring the story to an end; but it did bring an easing of the intensity to some degree. The desperate feeling of grief was lifted from my chest, clearing the way to attempt the next massive leap in my abilities.

Daniel wasn't the only relationship gift I would be given at the new corporation. My "boss" was in fact the first. Quite honestly one of the most honorable and kind souls I have ever met in this lifetime, William became my partner in the business field of interaction on the physical plane. Daniel was only a year older than I was, but William was about fifteen years my senior. I had pointed out at my first job interview with him that he could either hire a secretary or me. He could have a true partner to build this corporate division of the companies or a simple assistant.

He chose the partnership.

And I became a protector in his world, with skills in business beyond his that would allow him to build anything he wanted.

On the day that Daniel's company was officially purchased and handed security responsibilities for both executives and the 'floor,' William found himself in a scary situation. We dealt regularly with big business and big money consulting as a corporation. Lots of angry clients facing transitions. Hence the need for heightened security. And on this odd occasion, William (the marketing guy) had received a threatening letter. In biblical, crazy verse it insinuated that they were targeting the life of his teenage son. Not something to be taken lightly. And I deployed the security boys to both William's residence and on site to investigate and take precautions.

Daniel was out of town. A police officer was also brought in to discuss things. A closed door meeting with Shane and William in the security office... a meeting that Shane thought I *wasn't* invited to. I stared him down at the door, silently daring him to deny me entry even as William confirmed he needed to let me in. This little face-off is something we will discuss later, as it's an important factor for any 'intuitive' who thinks that working with the alpha males of law enforcement will be an easy road. But for now, let's stick to the main point of the story because what was about to happen forced me to make a life-changing choice.

I sat and listened to the police officer ramble from total ego about his 'take' on the situation. I appreciated his showing up, but as I 'read' the situation, I can tell you he was completely incorrect. What the exact accurate details were I couldn't tell you without finding a quiet corner, dropping into altered state and 'looking'...but this room wasn't conducive.

We shook hands with the officer and thanked him for coming. Pointless as the exercise had actually been. William and I walked down the hallway together afterward and I could feel his worry. He handed me the letter, now wrapped in plastic.

"Will you read this and tell me what you think is going on?"

I hesitated for a second. Was he actually asking me to…

"Give me 10 minutes in quiet space in my office," I replied.

I was going to do it. I knew I was. And after a few minutes in altered state I reappeared back in his office, closing the door behind me.

This could cost me my career.

I couldn't tell him without revealing myself that the police officer was wrong; and that it was actually *not* a man, but a little old lady pissed at his kid for doing something akin to trampling her rose bushes.

And *Jeez*. Who was I to think I was even getting that *right*? Because if I was wrong and some lunatic shot his kid…

But I was going to leap off the bridge to potential career suicide anyway, and reveal my psychic abilities. How could I not?

He not only took it well, but in a rare display of not-so-male sentiment, admitted that somehow he had always known about my abilities. That the day he hired me felt like important destiny to him. My resume had sat on his desk for nearly 9-months until the timing was right.

This demonstration of admitting to feeling a higher-hand in it all would not really surface so blatantly again. Our relationship would strengthen to great depth in the years to come though, as certainly as the mysterious threat to his son would vanish.

And wasn't *this* new situation both a completely empowering miracle and terrifying circumstance all at the same time. A soul-level partnership with a corporation founder, *and* the head of international security. Was this the set-up that my abilities were born for?

I would have to say that one of the most amusing first meetings I have ever witnessed would be the first time I put William and Daniel in a room together.

They were there to review a confidential list I had provided that outlined the internal executives backgrounds as well as identifying those I knew psychically were a threat. I called them *the sharks*, and my ability to read people's intentions made it easy for me to give both Daniel and William a list of those executives who held the intention to do harm, embezzle funds, etc. It was a new experience for all of us.

For me, I had to trust my intuition outside of private classrooms. For Daniel, was the new task of monitoring over a hundred executives and building security while inserting the input of a psychic's advanced warnings. Warnings that couldn't be acted on until an actual crime was committed complete with supporting evidence. And for William, there was the responsibility of trying to keep the corporation on track in both a business and moral sense. Oh yeah, and his "Communications Liaison" was a *psychic*. Holy cow.

The funny part, and one I hadn't entirely considered until standing in a room with them, was how two males complete with deep protective instincts were going to react to *each other*.

And I can tell you it was like two male lions facing off on the savannah. Territory needed to be claimed…which was tough, because I sort-of belonged to both of them.

I "read" them as their energies met.

William thought the young pretty-boy from security was trying to use me, sleep with me, whatever.

Daniel had soul-level recall of being my husband. That plus a good solid few months of intense training on how to flat-out protect me had unspoken words flying across the room.

I left so they could talk in private and get to know each other, but would be told later that William was the one who would put it almost immediately on the table. The older of the two lions setting the rules, with his paternal energy and intentions fully visible.

"You know what she can do."

"Yes."

"And you understand it needs to be handled carefully and with respect."

"Yes."

"Good."

And the business part of the meeting commenced.

The Path to Africa

We weren't going to England.

Whatever this relationship with Daniel-the-bodyguard was actually meant for, the end goal was not to take me back to England. In a private session with one of my international British Instructors the Guides were clear that I shouldn't go *with* him, and I definitely shouldn't try to do it *without* him. I was notified that there was something else approaching that both of us needed to deal with. Not to mention that at this point if we had been alone in a foreign country, I doubt we could have resisted sleeping together. Another bad idea. But to be frank, my guides seemed to be equally concerned with my health. It had gotten steadily better between the energetic presence of a Lifemate and my improving mental and emotional viewpoint. But I was told that if I tried to go train in the village on the North Sea in England alone, I would be ripped apart by the difficulty of not having him with me both energetically and physically.

It made sense. Not that I was happy with being denied my return to England. And Daniel was shocked when I slammed on the breaks. I explained pieces of it to him, minus the whole we-so-can't-have-sex part, and on the day we would have been scheduled to leave, our "why memo" was literally delivered at the office.

A new outside security client was brought in for an interview. He was a doctor with dual American and African citizenship that had decided he wanted to return to his home country in Africa to run for President. Tired of sending in medical aid to his home village and others and watching the corrupt and violent government steal it, he felt he could make more of a difference if he achieved appointment to a political office.

This was a monumental undertaking from a security perspective and Daniel, Mark, Shane and the rest of the security team would need to coordinate intensive security during transit and on location in Africa during the political elections. A country named by Time Magazine as having the longest, bloodiest war on the planet over the last 25-years. Rape, genocide and other atrocities were a daily occurrence. The current dictator had killed his father to claim the office of President. And the boys were about to get on a plane to do the first reconnaissance work. *Daniel was going to this terrible place.* Despite their backgrounds, I knew that all the Intelligence and Navy Seal training in the world wasn't going to make me feel any better about it. And I had to figure out what I was supposed to do with this situation besides stand back and hold my breath.

"Show me Africa."

I sat at home in my meditation chair.

Daniel and Mark were preparing to leave on their first trip to locate a residence for their Presidential candidate client, and secure it for the upcoming elections. Two men with skills but no military backup. It seemed insane to me. So I was sitting very tenuously in altered state.

Could I help this situation? Give them information to protect them?

I've learned when my radar goes off this strongly about a situation, that something bad is about to happen. A chain of events initiated that will produce unforeseen and potentially devastating results. And it was friggin' *Daniel* getting on that plane. I didn't know if my abilities extended to seeing the future of a situation by-request; but for a lifemate, I was willing to push the door open and find out.

"Show me Africa," I repeated, speaking to Spirit

I saw the savannah but was brought fairly immediately to the north eastern coast of the continent. Several helicopters flew in formation. This didn't make sense because the country they were going to was not coastal. I assumed I was just making it up. Then I watched as two of the helicopters crashed.

I leaped in consciousness and panic back to the room.

They were going to die in a helicopter crash?!

I walked around and analyzed. Imagination based on fear or was it a vision?

I was irritated and confused. Perhaps I didn't have any skills in this area after all. So why get worked up about it.

I walked into the office the next day and dropped a breakfast sandwich on Shane's desk. Our morning routine when time allowed, since he was stuck in the security office. I always tell my students that spirit will get you the information you need through any channel they can control, and as it stood, Shane was an easy mark. And about to drop a bomb on me c/o my guides.

"Oh my god, did you see the news this morning!" He launched into conversation as he paced, clearly upset by something. "Two helicopters crashed off the northeast coast of Africa yesterday…and I *knew* some of those guys."

I flashed cold then hot, and had to remind myself to breath.

The two helicopters I had seen in my vision…and connected to one of the boys.

Spirit was making a point.

Sit again. Take the vision further.

Be more specific in your question.

Yes, you can look into the future.

So I tried again.

This time with pad and paper in hand I shifted into altered state and saw several things clearly… *Mark was going to get really sick. Their hotel room wasn't safe, and they needed to keep important things with them at all times if they left it. And someone was going to run out of necessary medicine.* There may have been other elements involved in the communication, but this seemed to be the most important points.

I would love to tell you that I was brave enough to just dump all of that information on Daniel, but I didn't. I was uncertain if I was accurate and didn't want to risk being wrong in front of him. Besides, he was stressed out and managing the situation from his point of view, so I settled for typing it all up in an email and sending it to a friend. She was also a medium and intuitive and agreed to be my witness like we did in classrooms. To see if the future would turn out as I had seen it.

A month passed and several short, followed by extended trips were made by a mix of the security detail. Daniel made it home safely.

Then came the confirmations.

Mark, the ex-Navy Seal who *never* gets sick, was violently ill on arrival in Africa for 2-3 days. Their room had been searched as the current government officials investigated and became nervous with their presence and intentions to challenge the current dictator. And on another extended trip, Shane had run out of malaria medicine.

Jeez.

I wasn't sure if I should be enthusiastic or freaked out that I got all of those details right. I did believe though that in great part, I had allowed the activation and use of my abilities because it was my lifemate that was in danger. Not that I can't call on them again under less intense circumstances, but I wasn't going to run around doing this on a regular basis without great purpose. Unlike many of the intuitives I've seen that constantly attempt to turn their abilities into a cash-producing venture; I take all of this very seriously and know it comes with great responsibility. I don't initiate anything without it being requested from a higher place. I work at the soul-level and planetary-level, not the surface-human level.

9 Days

They were in trouble.

I had insisted all corporate employees complete the security profiles that included personal and medical information such as blood type. Ironic and a foreshadowing that the Public Relations chick was the one to be pushing security protocols. We had added a second, competing segment of security to the corporations as they continued expansion and purchasing of additional international companies; and this second group didn't get along with Daniel's team.

Alpha male crap.

The second group was comprised of ex-FBI, ex-NSA, ex-Secret Service. It had turned the place into a war zone with the Africa security detail right in the middle of it. Operators vs. Suits. Like they needed an internal challenge in the face of the external one.

But now I was getting a call that they wondered if *I* was in possession of the profile paperwork for three of the last security team to go to Africa.

I did the math. They were late coming home.

I had kept an eye on things from an office in the marketing division off site, though my relationship with all of the security guys had become stressed in the ensuing war and bad behaviors. Bottom line…they didn't like a female coming up with new security ideas and protocols…even if they are necessary and make sense. They also didn't like that I managed to find holes in their security system. Which I frequently did. And what they were *really* uncomfortable with in the end was how much they didn't understand about intuitive abilities. They were afraid of me on certain days of the week. Even Daniel, who wanted the info but was sometimes freaked into thinking that I could stand in a room and read everyone's minds.

Great.

So I had backed off a bit…until now.

Because William was at the main corporate headquarters office and three of the guys were missing in Africa. So I wasn't taking no for an answer. No matter who I pissed off.

My first check-in at the Tower (a.k.a. corporate headquarters) brought the meeting I really needed. Daniel stepped into the elevator on my way out and we had a few private moments alone. It hadn't been deliberate, but divine timing would probably be an accurate assumption in my world.

He stood professional until the doors closed, and then collapsed back against the wall, letting out a long breath.

"What happened," I simply asked.

He rubbed his eyes. The exhaustion and pain rolling off of him in waves.

"I *lost* them. For the last three days we didn't even know if they were alive!"

Anguish didn't begin to describe the level of guilt he was obviously struggling with as head of operations for this security detail.

"I don't know if we can get them back. It could take *months*, if they don't execute or starve them to death. They're claiming to the press that they've captured a team of Americans attempting to overthrow the government. They're going to be tried for treason as a way to stop our candidates Presidential run." Keith had broken protocol and brought his old Secret Service badge with him. It had been found. This put them in a whole new level of confused danger as the uneducated presidential guard thought they had someone like James Bond in custody.

Daniel admitted, as he would with no one else, that he had sat on the bathroom floor at home the night before and cried. Beyond the alpha male security persona, he carried deep sensitivity. We talked for a few minutes as we exited into the parking garage, then he went on to his next meeting.

I didn't quite make it to my car before throwing up. Three cheers for the empathic abilities. I had taken as much of his pain away to help strengthen him as I could, then was surprised by the violent release needed to clear it from my solar plexus. This was obviously going to be a rough ride. And I was going to have to figure out if calling on my abilities was an option to help save my team.

I walked into the 'Situation Room' as it was called, as if I had permission to be there. It took a couple of in-and-out appearances, and they didn't let me stay for certain briefings. But I finally obtained permission from the head of the corporations to be there. The security boys weren't happy, but I wore them down and eventually won the battle. In large part because they had bigger problems. Three of our guys… one operator from Daniel's team, one ex-secret service and one ex-cop had been taken hostage by the African Dictator along with about 15 other random South African hired security guys. And the Situation Room was lit up like NORAD with wall screens, phones, computers and every resource we could pull together to try and get them back…which was formidable.

It was like waking up in the middle of a Tom Clancy movie. There were men both in the room and on the phones in-country who went by code names and never revealed their "street identities." We had ongoing communications with American Embassies in multiple countries, the Red Cross, and even the White House. It became clear very quickly that with the exception of a well-meaning Red Cross, that there was no government office willing to publically help us or be associated with the situation. (Now there's a wake-up call to keep in mind if you're ever in trouble and traveling outside the United States.) So we set about putting immense pressure on the African Dictator through phone calls, use of the media and other private contacts. I did what I could to assist. Wrangling the media for press conferences, bringing in food, and even calling on some of my own contacts and resources, or jumping on the phone when they needed a 'different' voice to make a communication.

We were at day five when I finally texted Daniel for a private conversation.

"I know you're not going to come right out and ask me...but if you want me to 'look' at the situation, I will."

In the last few days I had felt him run the full gamut of emotions from pissed I was standing in his situation room without clearance, to relieved I was close. But this hadn't encouraged any real private conversations.

"Are we going to get them back? How long will it take?" came his quick reply. Apparently he wasn't pissed enough to not take advantage of a chance at some answers.

Ironic as that moment was, I shocked him back.

"I'm on a date right now. I'll 'sit' when I get home later."

He had that coming.

We all were taking necessary turns in the situation room, and I doubly was attempting to have a 'life outside of Daniel." He was married with one of those jealous insecure wives, and I needed to detach. So on a solo excursion to the gun range; I had met a nice SWAT-guy that I was now exploring the possibilities with.

No Daniel, my world does not *revolve around you*, was the underlying message.

But later I would 'sit' with spirit to see if I could get some answers for all of us.

Not unlike the show-me-Africa visioning from a month or so ago, I stepped into altered state to ask a few questions.

I saw the specific 'karma' being grounded for the three men held in captivity, and one additional supremely clear answer. The number 8 and the number 9 with regard to how long it would take to get them back. I wondered why they were giving me two numbers instead of one. I translated my guess to Daniel.

"I think you'll get them back this weekend at the 8-9 day marker," I told him.

He didn't believe me.

I could tell because instead of preparing to retrieve them through customs, airports and preparing medical transport, he set about giving just about everyone the weekend off to rest... including himself.

Nice.

As I've mentioned, people want to know what the psychic has to say, but don't necessarily believe it in a law enforcement or security setting. Which I think is too bad, because it could make for a wonderful team addition. I had once had a conversation with Mark, the ex-Navy Seal about use of intuition. He loved the book I gave him on power vs. force but still fully admitted that he thought I was weird. This was a highly decorated and internationally known warrior in his career with the Navy, and I flat out asked him one day if he denied that he used his instincts, intuition and knowingness in combat. He had seen quite a bit of battle. This was met with no such admission out loud, but I could feel him internally needing to consider my point.

So now, with a strong belief that my vision would be correct, I stood on a Saturday night with a skeleton crew (minus Daniel, of course) in the Situation room.

And the word came in.

They were being released without a ransom request because we had put enough pressure on the Dictator that he was scared to continue to hold them.

They were all in bad shape. Sick and starved. *I* packed the actual medical bag, sent the private doctor off to meet his flight, and helped locate a pilot to fly our private medical evacuation flight from Paris.

Released on day 8.

Arrived home in the United States on day 9.

Fall of the Empire

For the next year or two I would use the resources of the international corporations to assist as many people as I could. I initiated unique programs that evaluated security in relation to Public Relations initiatives, aimed at building internal and external corporate communication structures to assist newly acquired businesses to rebalance, and much more. Of particular interest to me was the opportunity to work with international human relief and aid organizations. Corporate funds were available, and I assisted on the communications-side with special event logistics, protocols for greeting international guests and coordinating security.

Not all of it was welcomed, as internal corporate power-struggles and greed escalated. In an effort to protect myself I worked in larger part with the Marketing group. I set this group of 18 creative staff up in cushy offices with all the comfortable amenities and freedom necessary to work and provide for the massive array of acquired companies in need of services.

But it wasn't to be a wonderful experience.

Instead, an insane number of people across the corporations and 99% of the marketing group would choose to display the worst levels of vicious behaviors I had ever seen. They made the security group brawls look like diplomacy in comparison.

They would pay a price for treating each other the way they did. The universe always taking care to see that energy-out can only be grounded on the person who initiates it. A fact that in large part has been my only peace in life when observing the terrible deeds people inflict on each other.

I've come to see the great opportunity and 'test' inherent in what transpired. A large group of souls all given the chance to use their talents and resources to serve each other and the world.

In a reading later with spirit they admitted that "it had gone too far." I, personally, took a tremendous beating and was attacked repeatedly and viciously as I stood as Corporate Communications Liaison and a Director. I was one of the few unafraid to walk onto a room and stand between the abusers and the abused. I wrote company-wide internal newsletters that suggested treating each other well amidst chaos.

Metaphysical studies all cater to the notion that everything is in divine timing; and while that may be true; humans on the earth plane are given opportunities to demonstrate good behavior and progress at a soul level or not. Light workers like me who stand on the rim and interact with those humans provide such opportunities. We may be asked to just bear witness, or step into the mix to engage directly to provide options, reminders and instruction. Regardless of the battles and horrible behaviors raging around me, I held the light…and my ground.

As the massive empire of companies fell to the ground, more than 3,000 employees would loose their jobs and many, also, their health insurance. I would exit safely with William and start a new company... health insurance intact, but greatly shaken and shocked by the choices people had made. Did they think there wouldn't be a price?

Closing the Doors

With the fall of the Empire, also went some key relationships in my life.

Daniel and I went our separate ways physically, though it would be a few months before I realized his coming to me *energetically* was still occurring often and I would have to put a stop to it. His behavior in the end was disappointing in its own way. On several very pointed occasions he had used me for information and resources and then not protected me from live-fire when it was within his power to stand up and do what was right. At an intensive private metaphysical session to be followed by training, one of my British instructors was shocked to see that an actual 'portal' was still open between Daniel and I despite the fact that we were physically separated. It was a door he would use to constantly come to me as he had before when he needed support energetically, mentally or emotionally.

It wasn't appropriate.

Yes, I loved him. But he had made his choices and he didn't get to keep me constantly on edge when he was incapable of standing beside me in friendship, or standing up to demand the life he wanted. Believe me, it's cruel enough to get introduced to a lifemate who's *married* to someone else; but to have them coming to you constantly can leave the pain a constant presence.

It had to stop. The gate would be closed.

In the metaphysical intensive I was participating in that same week, I consciously felt Daniel enter at one point as I worked in deep altered state. One of my guides stepped between us protectively, and I took the opportunity to look at him and directly close the gate.

"You don't get to do this. You can't keep coming back here. You left. You have a wife. You may not be happy there, but you don't get to continue to walk with me while not choosing to face yourself. This door is now closed."

And he was removed.

Or so I thought.

For all of you who work in altered state and wonder if the declarations you make actually connect to other people or initiate change on other planes, what happened next should fascinate you as much as it did me.

About a week later, I took a homeopathic remedy in greater strength than I'm used to, to rebalance and sleep. This particular type and dosage, I've noticed, allows me a heightened astral projection and lucid dreaming ability combination.

It was about 4:00am and raining buckets outside. I was awakened by a knock at the front door and went to see what was going on. This isn't a time of night I usually get visitors, and certainly don't open the door for them. I looked out the security glass and was surprised to see Daniel standing there impatiently, with one had against the brick wall.

I opened the door and he stepped inside. He smelled good. His t-shirt was wet from the rain and tropical night humidity. I made some comment about being half asleep and was he *kidding* about showing up at this hour...?

He was nervous and treading carefully, yet obviously upset about something.

I hugged him to ward off whatever emotions were chasing him and it gave him the courage he had been looking for.

"You can't *do* that. You can't close the door and lock me out," he held me tight in his panic. God it felt good to be in his arms. Both absolutely natural, and yet strange considering the hour.

"Are you *real*," I whispered against his neck.

He froze.

Apparently this sort of nighttime visit was a regular thing *astrally*, but for all my abilities, I hadn't been entirely aware of it. He realized in that moment that for the first time I *was* suddenly conscious of what was happening, and he was bracing for my reaction.

I shifted in his arms and kissed him. He responded. And *nothing* in my life has ever felt more right in the sense of two souls that fit together. But as he started backing me up toward the bedroom I called a halt to it by asking a simple question…

"Where is your *wife*?"

The spell was broken and I woke up.

I had said no.

The door was now truly closed.

Sometimes it amazes me that I'm still standing.

Through it all. I would get shot (metaphorically speaking), and then ask what the next 'assignment' was. In truth, there was now a great need for a recovery period, which I would be provided with to some extent through a career path that granted me a home office. But the approach of the end of the Mayan Calendar and opportunity to assist humanity in transition was only a handful of years away, so my personal and metaphysical expansion pushed forward.

In addition to my choice to finally leave Daniel behind, came the gut-wrenching realization that I must also leave my birth parents behind. My grandmother at Stansted Hall had been correct. They weren't being nice to me. And I had been correct also…they weren't going to accept the news of my expanded metaphysical abilities with any sort of grace. My dad had angrily "accidentally" hung up the phone *four* times during my discussion about what had transpired in England, with my mother still on the other line making random excuses for him. She played her part to perfection. Actually, and without knowing it, reenacting an exact scene from the movie X-men II, which had long ago become my natural example of how certain things seemed to be evolving for me.

"Well, honey…you could choose a *different* destiny," she had sweetly offered. It was an insane suggestion. First of all, my mother didn't use words like 'destiny' in a sentence as she recoiled from all but non-daily activities or historical recollections. And secondly…are you *kidding* me…?!

Hmmm.

I can choose to stay in a human environment of illusion, struggle and little support, OR, I can walk with amazing beings of light that love me unconditionally.

Guess which option I choose.

And from that point forward their bad behaviors would escalate. Not just about me though. They didn't deal with their own anger, fear and other issues so the self-inflicted pain was just grounded by lashing out on each other AND me.

No way.

So the day that my shaman friend and her guides had 'journeyed' for me to deal with the original Daniel-past-life-issue, she also took the opportunity to go to battle for me with my mother. I had been having more and more trouble letting her physically touch me. Feeling deep, rancid tendrils of energy connecting us and constantly draining me. But my mother wasn't going to be energetically disconnected from me without a fight. She was desperate to maintain her control and connection. But in the end, the link was successfully severed. What an amazing relief. My skills are strong, but sometimes we need other light workers to assist us in larger endeavors and life shifts. I'm grateful that this level of assistance was provided for me.

From there, came the painful letter and actual physical notification I had to send. She blamed me for my father's bad health and more. I was shaking with both fear and relief, and though certain that I had to do this for my own soul growth, wondered how I was going to live with no physical family. My knowingness translated to years of reality with my brother. He would be angry and not understand my choice. And for awhile, he did make me doubt myself. This apparently didn't sit well with my Guides, who suggested rather emphatically about six months later that I contact my parents and offer one last chance at a relationship if they could stop the negativity.

I found this unbelievable. Guilt was riding me though, and I always follow guidance. Little did I know that the *reason* my Guides wanted me to try to return was so that I would be rid of that guilt forever. On the surface it seemed like they wanted reconciliation. I certainly didn't want to go back to the abuse though. So I settled for sending an email to ask if they would like to just be a happy family.

The response was amazing.

Apparently they had finally sought out psychological counseling! I was thrilled. For about 10 seconds. Until I continued on in my mother's letter to discover that they had done this to figure out what was wrong with *me*. Somehow my nurse-mother had gotten some psychologist-friend to actually diagnose me as bi-polar. *Medication* was actually suggested. This, by the way, is illegal to even suggest without having completed a physical examination.

Of course this would be their reaction.

Because there was nothing wrong with *them*, after all. I'm actually surprised they didn't shoot for some sort of schizophrenia diagnosis. But a part of me knew they had seen enough proof to be afraid to play their game with that level of disrespect.

And another door in my life was emphatically and permanently closed.

I Walk for My People

Finally released from the ties of physical-plane-family, I returned to focusing on my 'family' on the non-physical plane. In reality, I am the *least* alone person on the planet in any given moment regardless of physical relationships or circumstance. A fact I'm constantly grateful for.

I stepped next into what would be my last metaphysical training intensive in a formal classroom hosted by the British instructors. I didn't know that at the time, but I was aware of the undercurrent of negative energy building and brought in by groups of new students from another city. Bad behaviors abounded, and I held tight to my Guides through the exercises. I also felt a deeper change in the air. Theses classrooms were becoming less pure and more rancid. Amplification of unshed negative patterns was obvious. The universe wasn't going to allow these patterns to stand forever on the unseen mental and emotional planes. Not with the approach of 2012 and the energies speeding up. And I was shocked to observe that even the advanced British instructors were starting to wage war visibly on each other. This was the time I knew we had all trained for. A time when the pressures and earth changes would require we stand in our mastery. But as I looked around, I felt like I was the only one who seemed to know that.

I stayed close to my Guides and Guardians and demanded the space I needed from the reindeer games. I wondered why I had been told to attend this training. The answer would surprise me. This would be my last. It was time for me to realize the last few pieces necessary to stand on my own…and begin to *teach*.

Mixed in with regular exercises, my primary British instructor insisted that I stand up more than once and actually provide tandem instruction with him. This was *not* the norm. It was, however, exactly what I needed to cement the understanding that I was more than capable of doing so. This realization, plus one monumental altered state exercise would shift my viewpoint forever, as to who and what I was.

Four of us were sitting in a close circle to enter into an altered state exercise together. Two of the others, Kim and Justine, were long-time acquaintances for me in these classrooms. They say rewards always follow massive transition points and courageous acts, similar to walking down an aisle for 'graduation.' I have seen that to be true, but also know these deliveries and moments can come in unexpected forms.

As I dropped deeply into the energies present, I followed basic instructions that we were to initiate a 'walk into the future' to see where our lives would be taking us in the next five-plus years. I always take these directives with a grain of salt knowing that my personal team of Guides will use the opportunities to communicate whatever was actually necessary regardless of any lesson plan.

I found myself standing on the observation deck of a huge ship hovering above the earth's atmosphere. This was a place I was familiar with, and go to often. I can relax here, outside the immediate earth plane where human chaos and thought forms are a constant assault on my senses. This place on the ship carries the energy of 'home.'

But the view was a bit different this time. In addition to the ship I was standing on, I could see two other distinct 'groups' working out across the planetary horizon. My instant awareness was that they each were a different 'race' of beings, and each could be seen at different working levels, sending energy and resources down to the planet surface. I noticed that Kim, who physically sat to my left in the small circle, was a part of one of the races working with sacred geometry and symbol. And Justine, who physically sat to my right, was with the second group of beings at work. Of great clarity in this vision was the presentation that we each were not from earth, and came from completely different races with different jobs. This was further demonstrated by showing the physical positioning of the groups and ships at different levels and distances above the planet. All in all it was a fascinating sight to watch the coordination occurring between them.

The view was as clear in its detail as a bright sunny day walking down the street. I was no stranger to these awareness's, but did in fact just mentally set them aside in the past or enjoy them for the vacation-moments they seemed to be. I figured I had enough to struggle with in human form without delving too deeply into the possible ramifications of an extra-terrestrial connection.

As we came 'back' following the exercise, the instructor circled the room to check in with the groups to see what they had experienced. In theory, these practitioners were all supposed to have been aiming at gathering pieces to assist each other. I was surprised to discover however, that instead of the usual supportive caring-and-sharing, there was mostly anger and emotion flooding the room. Individual students lashed out at each other. Fear and either an unwillingness or inability to 'see' ran rampant. At one point, two students actually argued in raised voices and we thought it would escalate to a physical altercation. It was insanity. Another confirmation provided for me that these metaphysical classrooms were beginning to degrade.

The exception in every way to the mass negativity of the other twenty-eight or so students in the room was to be found in my small group of four. We were to learn that with the exception of the one random new girl who was a youngster and admitted to 'seeing nothing,' Kim, Justine and I had had the *exact* same vision. Three separate extra-terrestrial races, three different physical levels of work and positioning, and each of us from one of those very specific groups. It was a little bit breath-taking, actually. Even the rancid negative behaviors around the room came to a halt as we described it in vivid detail. I'm not sure if they were frightened of us or knew that respecting what had been shown and accomplished was the appropriate response. Regardless of the room, I was personally feeling a sudden shift in my own energy. It was as if in that moment I had agreed to accept who and what I was, as well as what was to come and what it was for.

A certainty of purpose and power I had never felt previously moved through me as the room cleared for the lunch break. Kim and Justine were quiet and went separate ways. I sat alone for a few minutes in the big room before exiting to walk down the long hallway to the exterior courtyard doors. It, too, was now empty.

I heard the whispers clearly and repeated it out loud as I stood between the two worlds and remained still connected, in part, to the vision. So many times I had cried and asked what the point of the lifetime was. Now I knew a big puzzle piece.

I walk for my people. This was my graduation.

The Wolf... Past & Present

The little girl clutched at the edge of her brownie uniform in a nervous gesture that no one was actually present to see with the exception of the trees standing like silent sentinels across the wooded area. It was quiet. The only noises were the crunch of autumn leaves beneath her tiny sneakers, and the occasional sound of laughter coming from children in other parts of the park.

Why had she chosen to do this? To wander away from her Girl Scout troop. Into the trees and down the hill that lead to the wolf perimeter. They had been given specific warning not to go near this place, because the animals were wild and dangerous. Perhaps it had been the pressure of the other two girls that had started her into the woods; but now, long after the others had fled in fear, she felt drawn to complete the journey alone. Something she *never* did, in part because at age seven she was afraid of nearly everything; and also because she *always* followed the rules set down by the adults.

She hadn't seen any wolves on this trip to the zoo, their enclosure stretching out for a few square miles to give the pack room to run. The guide had said they preferred not to come near the humans, so a sighting wasn't to be expected that afternoon.

But she *really* wanted to meet one.

A decision that seemed unreasonably important now given the circumstances, as she moved closer to the forbidden fence anyway.

The animal broke without warning through the underbrush and landed not far from where she was standing, nearly scaring the life out of her. She considered running until logic merged together with some crazy version of certainty. *The fence would protect her... but he wouldn't have hurt her anyway.*

He closed the gap by fifty, thirty, and then twenty feet before coming to a halt. His fur quivered, and he was breathing hard. Even to her young observance this creature was wild, and she watched him shiver slightly as if deciding what to do...charge or retreat? She knew the second the wolf had made his decision to do neither. Instead, a flow of unspoken communication began between them, eye-to-eye and soul-to-soul. An agreement perhaps, from the spirit of the wolf who held the energy of "the teacher." Something shared that would be used, required and called upon from within this child years later. And no one ever knew about the encounter beyond the spirits who shared it.

It was time to teach. I stared at my computer screen with tired eyes and marveled at the amount of work the last few months had been in setting up the metaphysical company, website, curriculum, materials, locations and reservations system. No chore for the faint of heart or anyone who didn't know all the levels of admin, marketing and logistical event planning that my corporate career had graced me with. And I was running the usual program. Accomplish a whole year of work for every month that passed. Divine timing seemed to be requiring a much faster tempo to keep up with these days. And added to actually teaching up to 25 students per class at least once per month in between other corporate work was an exhausting pace.

The fantastic news was that I had narrowed down my potential teaching partners to just one, and William had amazingly agreed to financially support this new metaphysical company. So in all areas I seemed to have everything I needed to do it. But William had always been like that with me. With no metaphysical experience what-so-ever, and certainly no real conscious belief in my "woo-woo" stuff; he still supported whatever path I declared I needed to take with little question.

The part that *did* come as a shock to me was how territorial and unfriendly other metaphysical instructors got when faced with anything they view as competition. I suppose I never considered this because I firmly believe that the planet is a really big place with an insane number of souls needing support. *And weren't we all in this together...?*

Apparently *not,* turned out to be the resounding and unanimous reaction.

I spent years training with a group of about 45 pretty highly-functioning practitioners, and the second I announced I was going to start teaching I was no longer welcome in the group or treated with kindness.

Jeez.

Wasn't learning as much as possible and then taking it out into the world the whole point of all those years of training...?

Again, apparently not.

But there was one wonderful and obviously more advanced soul left standing after my announcement that I was going to teach, and that I was looking for a partner to tandem teach *with*. My second firm belief, as it stood, was that I felt it was so very important to have at least two instructors in a classroom. This allows for much greater depth of work for everyone. Multiple perspectives and abilities to benefit the students. And with curriculum stuff often bringing up difficult issues in-between lesson materials, it's critical to have a healer in the room to assist with balancing and direct nurturing when release-situations arise.

All-in-all, beyond the initial human dramas at the beginning, Maggie and I were excited to find we were a wonderful team. And this lead to a free-flowing of work with spirit that included magic both in private classroom settings and in what I would call "excursion" classes. I set up these on-location destinations to give students (and us), a chance to do things that I've never seen in metaphysical curriculums. This included altered state work in the direct presence of ancient artifacts from past civilizations like the Mayans, Incans, Africans and Native Americans. The opportunity was also provided to sit in the same room to meditate, do energy-work, physically touch, and initiate telepathic communication with elephants, great horned owl, large reptiles, marsupials and more. We accomplished it all locally using the museums and zoos and setting up private encounters away from the public. Some of the animal handlers thought we were nuts, but excursion after excursion to unique venues allowed for some of the most fascinating learning experiences. Metaphysics merged with these encounters, and as an artist and healer who paints, I even gave students the opportunity to feel the energy of creating vortexes and painting in acrylic at a completely different level to open dimensional gateways.

At a point in the middle of all these adventures, I began to have a few 'encounters' of my own when alone in my home. Different than anything I'd experienced in the past, I began to 'see' a mysterious dog walking around the house. It was a different occurrence for me because rather than being a one-time event, I was *constantly* seeing him. Usually from the back, I could clearly see he had the hind quarters of a German Sheppard, though oddly, I never completely saw his face. Finally, after a few discussions with other friend-intuitives, I followed through on the realization that this was a real dog reaching out to me for assistance. And I knew where I would find him. He needed to be rescued from the county Humane Society.

Now, let's be clear about something before I go any further with the story.

I didn't *want* a dog.

Not the mess or the walks or the hassle. But I did want a partner. And excitement over training a service dog merged with knowingness that I had to act quickly. The urgency of the energy was intense and driving me nearly crazy. So that weekend I brought home a scared, half starved and very sick German Sheppard-collie mix I named Toby.

"Meant-To-Be," I had told the lady at the shelter after an exhausting movie-drama afternoon that included my being called upon to offer a life-behavioral-transition-point opportunity to an angry woman dying of cancer. She had, at first, tried to take Toby away from me. Then in a rare moment, had thrown her arms around me and yielded in tears. I knew this was a very important situation for her soul, and was honored, though exhausted by day's end, to have been called upon to play a necessary part in the opportunity spirit wanted to give her.

Metaphysical multi-tasking would be a good description for this type of circumstance, and I have long-since learned that you should never assume you know *why* spirit is asking you to do something or go somewhere. For whatever scenario is presented, there will likely be many additional surprise parts-and-pieces weaved into the whole of the experience before it's finished. And if you function at this level where you have trust and are instantly willing to follow knowingness and spirit requests, then the quantity and magnitude of those requests on any given day can be immense.

To whom much power is given, much will be asked.

I had now been 'gifted' with a wolf and was honoring my long-ago-made agreement to teach. With these two pieces merging together, Toby would also be joining us in direct classroom instruction to bring an aspect of interaction like nothing any of us had ever seen. His time with me would be as a *metaphysical* service dog rather than a physical one.

Enter the Shaman

Maggie was sick. Another 'sensitive' who had battled the earth plane elements and now faced the difficulty of a serious physical condition that might end the life walk. I wondered sometimes in private moments of pain and sorrow why the journey of service here had to be this rough for us.

So I stood before her now in a small private classroom where she had just revealed the truth to our students. I hadn't expected that. She was fiercely private, and wanted no special treatment or energy shifts in worry or sorrow to influence the relationships. The classroom today included healing work, and I was about to initiate a demonstration when I felt the pull-of-spirit that notified me that Maggie was to be the recipient.

I hesitated for a moment because she and I were usually careful not to "work on each other." We had respectful boundaries for both friendship and partnership. But whatever was about to transpire, the energy building in the room made us both certain it was the right path. Also of note to us was that the student level had been dropped down to only nine for the day, and a thunderstorm was brewing outside, as if declaring the arrival of something and the support of the elementals themselves.

We changed the room to only natural lighting, placed crystals where instructed to, and set up the aromatherapy infuser with a custom blend. We always combined all of the tools as guided prior to beginning a class or session. And from there, I stepped back behind Maggie away from the circle of students to find my 'energetic footing.' I had long since learned the importance of 'getting clear and centering' before starting a healing. There were always specific instructions. Touch or don't touch. Moments to wait for. Unlike reiki or structured intellectual-based techniques, I knew to let go and listen once entering into a trance-state. Nothing else would do. Knowingness would lead the dance. Intellect and structure may be good at first for entry or for beginners, but it greatly hinders Spirit's ability to deliver in-the-moment instruction and solutions. Healing through intellect is frequently muddied by ego, or at best turns it into a controlling-human process instead of a divine one.

I reached for my Guides and felt a surge of power that was strange and not entirely comfortable for me. Energetic lightning seemed to arc around me, and I shook at the strength of it. A normal healing this was obviously not to be; but instead, my first completely conscious merge with my black jaguar guide in direct healing. So much so, that beyond the music playing in the room and releasing any sort of attachment I may have had to structure, I allowed the physical healing session to take on an even deeper-than-usual life of its own.

Down for a moment to crouch on the floor, I opened to allow her to merge at every level and virtually take over. I had never done this before, and my personality took a moment to consider resistance and note that I couldn't *believe* I was allowing it to occur for the first time with an audience. It was then that I realized beyond any healing work, there was also a 'stand-off' necessary. That was evident in the discomfort I felt. It wasn't anger, but a determination and feeling that a warrior knows comes just before a battle. *Something needs to be taken care of...* it quietly notifies as the clairvoyant vision and sound of a sword being unsheathed could be heard to emphasize the message symbolically. The cat had always been one of my primary guardians that linked me strongly to my Mayan DNA, and now it seemed certain that I was being called upon as a Shaman to do soul recovery and extraction for Maggie.

In deep trance I vaguely recall feeling the cat within me, and engaging in both a spoken and unspoken conversation with an unwanted entity also present in the circle. The message I gave it was clear. *You are no longer welcome here. This is not appropriate. You don't get access to her anymore.* This was followed by another surge of activity and energy beyond me, and in a few moments I was aware that the entity had been removed and was no longer present. The extraction of pain from her body, then a flood of love ushered in the final steps. I completed this energy transfer for Maggie, and then slowly allowed the cat to carefully withdraw.

I don't know exactly how long the whole session took or every detail of what transpired; but this is actually the norm for anyone who works in moderate to deep trance. We aren't there to direct or intellectually play a role. We are there to completely let go and allow spirit to channel through in any way necessary. The other thing to know about such sessions is that a true 'healing' isn't provided to be an ending point or 'cure.' Instead, it's an opportunity. If the recipient allows, then some things can be worked with or cleared or strengthened. But if they don't deal with the root cause, or if they continue to engage in the thoughts or behaviors that lead to the illness, then all of the healing work in the world will be met with resistance and re-occurrence of dis-ease.

From our student's perspective, this viewing had been sort-of shocking. No boring, systematic reiki classroom here. They had gotten to see not only energetic, shamanic shape-shifting, but also soul recovery and extraction. The translation of what had occurred was that an entity had attached itself to, or was walking with Maggie in an inappropriate way and draining her. My team of guides in union with hers had taken the opportunity provided by the classroom to step in and deal with it using my energy and physical connection to accomplish the removal…among other things.

As confirmation of what I believed had transpired, Maggie relayed the feel of the jaguar's fur astrally against her knees when I had come close to work with her, and in the weeks that followed she would experience a noticeable strengthening of her physical body as well. It was a monumental 'gateway' experience for me in the use of my abilities. And it didn't escape my notice that once again I had been sort-of tricked into doing it.

Send her a life-and-death situation with someone she loves, and don't tell her in advance what the program will be. All slight-of-hand by my Guides aside, it was our willingness to leave classrooms at least 50% in open format that allowed for the most powerful spirit interactions possible.

Adventures In Teaching

There was a shifter in the house.

After the explosion of my 'shamanic' healing abilities, I could say with certainty that this was true. I had merged with my cat enough times now to make such a statement about another being. And this one was far from subtle. He was, in fact, hitting my senses and knowingness on multiple levels. His name was Matthew, and this was not the first time we had met. He was a healer and protector of my health and well-being, held the haunting familiarity and passion of a Lifemate, and brought the challenge of pushing me to use my heightened abilities. There was a wildness about our union and interactions similar to the rise of primal instincts that I knew must exist between two animals. I had certainly felt these types of responses within the depths of my cat. But jaguar was not the form that *he* actually shifted into when leaping from human form to animal.

Toby and I had just moved into a large house with vaulted ceilings and a huge open living room area that lent itself perfectly to working with student groups in a private setting. It also had crazy energy…and I don't entirely mean that in a good way. In addition to dealing with the new house I was also faced with transitioning my expectations about my new "partner." Toby was turning out to be a slightly different experience than I was expecting. As Caesar Milan, *the Dog Whisperer* so accurately says, "*The Universe doesn't give you the dog you want, it gives you the dog you need.*" Toby protected me and gave me courage while I did the same for him. It could certainly be said that both of us had lived through an abusive past, and rehab was definitely part of the process. This rather high-maintenance situation would be added to another shocking realization.

One day I turned to find him standing a few feet behind me, across the room, and displaying a stillness that was different somehow for him. I looked into his eyes and the feeling of the connection was like a bolt of lightning slamming through me. It wasn't Toby looking back at me, it was *Matthew*. I leaned back against the sink for support and wondered if I was loosing my mind. How much *crazy* can a person take in a life…? I wondered.

So I shifted my gaze to something else for a moment to try to blink the scene away.

But when I looked back it was still Matthew, merged so deeply with Toby that I think anyone could have felt the change-of-presence. I heard the whispers clearly. *Toby is a gift directly from Matthew. Matthew's shifted form is wolf. When necessary, he can merge with and use Toby to protect or lead you.*

It would take a few occasions of witnessing this change and dealing with the shock of suddenly seeing the dog look back at me with someone else's eyes before I would settle into a kind-of acceptance of it. But in reality, though I loved them both and couldn't have been more grateful, amazed and honored by the gift, I still found myself a bit stand-offish in Matthew's presence. If you recall our previous discussion about Lifemates, they are a powerful connection beyond the realm of soul mate to something deeper and stronger; and Mathew seemed to be present on at least one level to coax me onward in using my array of abilities. It makes me laugh now as I consider that some of the intensity was similar to cat vs. dog energy. Jaguars are solitary creatures, and though I resonate to wolf and have run with the pack, just try mixing all of *those* power energies in a room plus the additional energetic and life challenges occurring. It would clearly take a warrior and shifter of Matthew's magnitude to help me work through the emotions of it all in addition to the physical challenges that raged within my world. I can say with both gratitude and certainty that he displayed an incredible amount of patience.

In the evenings, in the strange energies of the new house, spirit would build and move to prepare for deep trance classes or just to meet my daily needs. I noticed that this seemed to include fending off negative planetary and house-residue energies as well. On some nights it would make Toby incredibly nervous; while on other nights it was fascinating just to watch him attentively follow the guides around from room to room as they worked. On one night in particular, I had the opportunity to work with the energy of dragon, but the appearance of the 25-foot tall creature sent Toby racing to hide in the guest bedroom. All-in-all he provided great confirmations, which I'm certain was part of the gift. And mercifully, when Matthew would appear to work with me in either sitting or moving meditation, Toby would calm down noticeably. *"Can you believe what you signed up for buddy...?"* I would ask him on less than quiet nights while we hugged and watched the show.

It was this build-up and movement of energies that set the stage for some amazing class-work in trance, meditation and more with our students. Working in the hotel meeting rooms and yoga centers had been productive. Working in the house where spirit worked 24-7 with me was a *ride*. As the earth changes were ramping up around the planet and economies crashing, our metaphysical progress marched onward and included a few powerful interactions that bear mentioning. They moved me along the path as certainly as they provided students with some amazing opportunities for expansion.

On one such occasion, I had been gifted by my brother with a hand painted Mayan calendar disk. In the form of a circle and made out of a very heavy wood material, it came directly from the jungles of Belize. I hadn't even known about his trip. The disk had been made by an artesian of Mayan descent from one of the local villages. When it was handed to me, I was shocked by the initial spirit explanation. *You didn't get to take the class to the ruins of Coba this year as you'd hoped to, so the Mayan energies have been brought to you.*
    A combination of situations including the drug wars in Mexico that destabilized the region and the declining value of the U.S. dollar had all added to the reason the journey had been removed from our options list. I was so honored to have this opportunity to work with the beings that had obviously inspired my brother to bring this piece back with him, and our next classroom at the house was a perfect fit.

Another addition that had been made to the private classrooms was Toby. Rehab for him, and an incredible opportunity for us. He was certainly our 'witness' and notified us of things going on in the room. As animals do, he carried the pure reaction to energies that could easily be seen and discussed.

In this time-travel classroom, with the Mayan disk from Belize placed in the center of the circle of students, I directed them to begin to shift into altered state to connect with the energies present. We had just started the slide into an eyes-closed meditative state when an unfamiliar growl brought us all quickly back to the room. Opening our eyes, we found that Toby had left his position beside Maggie to stand and confront something (or someone) that was standing over the Mayan disk. I had never seen him give this type of warning. He was suddenly all wolf, with a full display of fangs and gums as the warning rumbled low in his throat.

The great part about tandem teaching is that while I was more focused clairsentiently and holding the energy of the room for the students, it left Maggie free to work directly with Toby and use her clairvoyance. Between all of us, a clear picture came into view of what we would describe as a 6+ foot Neanderthal-like South American man. With animal skins for clothing, and a presence that had shifted Toby all the way back to a deep and primal state. Our classroom for the day was, in part, to allow connection to other times and places, and now it became clear that the disk provided a gateway of sorts to do just that.

Worlds Revealed

Perhaps it was the earth changes raging across the planet, or maybe the truth in pieces that needed to be provided to our students in a first wave of revealing. Somewhere, someone, always has to lead. I'd spent a lot of years holding that job title, and now can see that at times the encounters were designed to equally desensitize *me* through powerful and undeniable communications. Interactive opportunities that brought the *visitors* to the classrooms.

I, thankfully, was fortunate enough to be teaching with a partner who had apparently as much off-planet interaction as I did. We both carried a bit of denial in the daylight hours, but overall our deeper knowingness allowed for a natural pace and gentle energy to be instituted within the weirder moments. I also had been gifted with one student in particular named McKenzie who held both the energy in the room for me when needed, and balanced out for masculine-feminine polarities. And to top it off, he was *very* clairvoyant. Truly gifted beyond his conscious awareness, and mercifully without ego about it. This combination of abilities always helped me feel protected when I stepped into deep altered state work with him in a room. He would prove to be another longer-term partner, and bring a few mind-blowing confirmations to my trance-work-mergers as well.

We were approaching the end of the year, and everyone seemed to be wrestling with various issues in their life that could be felt in the exhaustion they carried both mentally and emotionally. It was 2008 and personal life-lesson work now was obviously a requirement rather than an optional participation avenue. It is also important to understand that at this point I was no longer doing private sessions or readings for students. I understood clearly the instructions I was being given in these end-times. That it was imperative to give students the tools to be self-sufficient and then require that they take self-responsibility for doing the work *themselves* on every level. The support would be present, but not to loiter in the past or continue to ignore personal issues. I worked at the soul-level. I did not hang out in the dramatic levels of the daily mundane or serve as some sort of ongoing life-counselor. And as Maggie and I worked with a core group of serious students, we discovered that we also had to deal with an array of those who where only there for the comfort or the 'high.' This sort of underlying true intention was never allowed by spirit to stand easily, or last in one of our rooms. Spirit used the access and opportunities to give every student soul-level important information. They may have come for the quick-fix or energy-high, but they often left with more than they bargained for. This information was *always* delivered with love, support AND the solution, of course; but that didn't guarantee that a student would be willing to actually *face* their own negative pattern issues and halt them. More likely than not they would disappear once provided with the notification and core solutions formula; some even lashing-out in anger. It was disappointing at best, but Maggie and I made a deal with spirit that we would keep offering the room until told directly by the guides to end it.

So for one of these house-based classrooms I agreed to do a full-blown deep trance channeling for about 15 of our students. I had come a long way since that first merge with my gatekeeper at Stansted, and now trusted her to come through herself or direct any interaction that might be needed.

Depth was achieved, with Maggie and Toby on my left and McKenzie powering and balancing the circle from the opposite side, directly across from where I was seated. My gatekeeper came through first with a general discussion, and then surprised me by focusing on one student at a time to work with more personally and answer questions. I was very pleased by the balance of energy and confirmed accuracy from my back-seat 'perch.'

When I thought it was finished, I was again amazed by guidance from my gatekeeper to maintain the level, even as she withdrew to stand behind me. There were others in the room to be recognized; some of the guides that had come for this rare chance to be introduced and speak directly to their charges. A group for Maggie and group for Claire were the most spectacular of note because they were clearly not from this planet. I personally, was still considering the possibilities and larger meaning of such interactions, including those meetings with my own guides-of-a-strange-origin. I wondered how this was going to fly with the 'kids' in the room. We weren't just using basic mediumship to talk to 'Uncle Bob' anymore.

The introduction to Maggie's 'people' was not at all shocking to her, but a few in the room who got the up-close-and-personal clairvoyant sighting admitted to being a bit frightened of them. About 3 ½ feet tall, disproportionally large heads with big dark eyes. I nearly jumped out of my chair when the first one appeared in front of me. They just teleported or moved at lightning speed from point to point and it was a little disconcerting. But their energy was very loving and I passed the telepathically relayed message to Maggie.

Not to be outdone, the next group of visitors came for Claire. Their energy was so drastically different it actually took me a few minutes to rebalance to it. There would not be discussions first with this introduction. Instead, one of the large creatures had received permission from my gatekeeper to initiate a physical-merge with me. This would apparently provide an unforgettable demonstration for those present. And I agreed, letting the 7-foot tall lizard-like being 'sit' within my body to feel it and see the room through my eyes. It was a remarkable sensation. My breathing even changed in depth and pace to match his reptile-like intake and outflow of air.

I allowed this merger for a few minutes, while he communicated only to me the message he wanted shared with Claire. I would give this to her in pieces, being careful in my wording due to the serious implications of the information and obvious history. I am always aware of the delicate nature of my job, and even more so on this day when it seemed spirit was taking every opportunity to make last-chance deliveries.

As you would expect, this was a group of beings that had worked and lived with Claire in past lifetimes. I could feel the history as clearly as their race's lack of emotion. They respected her, but were actually sent to stand watch in an attempt to help Claire to avoid the mistakes of her past.

Ok… and actually… if I were to just have said it like it was without the sugar coating, it felt like Claire had done something very inappropriate in a past incarnation and they were going to make sure she wasn't *allowed* to do anything like it again. I naturally would pass the message a great deal more gently than that. My job seemed to be shifting quickly from simple translator to Ambassador between worlds. The truth wouldn't be left out, but in many ways I would let the strong presence of these beings energetically relay the bulk of the message to her and the others in the room. Claire didn't admit out loud to actually having any familiarity with them, but I know there is no *way* and intuitive with even her basic skills didn't have a base-line knowingness. These beings were massive in size and energy, and regardless of denial, this introduction would not allow her to be dismissive in the future. Even in private moments should they decide to speak with her directly.

For me, aside from the *WOW* of the encounter on the internal planes, I had been told not to tell the students what had transpired from my perspective. I followed the instructions from my Gatekeeper to come back to the room and ask them to share first what *they* had just witnessed clairvoyantly. Denial for me was completely wiped off the option list when my star-clairvoyant McKenzie nearly leaped out of his chair in excitement and started the discussion off with:

"Oh my gosh, there was this huge Komodo Dragon creature standing on two legs and he walked over and sat right in your body…and even your breathing changed to totally match his deep reptile pattern!"

Nope. No denial available for me on *that* encounter.

Worlds Coming Undone

Maggie and I would work with students in direct classrooms for another year or so before being told that our jobs on this level were finished. I can't say I took it well at first. My 'human' belief had always been that I was on a path that would lead to larger size and quantities of direct interaction with students; not shrinking classrooms. I would see that our optimism was outpacing the reality were humanity was concerned. Reports of increasing rancid behaviors and degrading classrooms were coming in from all over just as clearly as economies and inappropriate corporations and financial systems were falling. It was clearly an ending cycle that held energies akin to the proverbial judgment day. Souls were pushing their personalities to face themselves and change, or have the-roof-ripped-off their lives as a tactical measure to bring situations to an end forcibly. It was astounding to watch.

For my part, I followed instruction to move Toby on to his 'forever home' with one of my students. Victoria was great with animals and would take him through the next stage of life and rehab. In truth, I had let Toby pick her. Over months of classes he had frequently gravitated to her and she even used to arrive early to take him for an early morning run before class. He and I had been an important union for the time we were together, but I felt that he deserved the opportunity to just be a dog and have fun without all the intensity. Victoria was a runner, and would take him for 3-mile morning and evening workouts. He even got a girlfriend out of the deal with the little corky-dog already in the house.

All-in-all his transition timing was important. The energies of the neighborhood were worsening as well. On one occasion I awoke at 3:00AM to some sort of disturbance on the other side of the house. I walked through the living room towards the guest bath just in time to feel what I would call an energetic lightning bolt slamming down into the hallway. It was unnerving and far from positive. I was getting the message loud and clear. It was time to move to a new sanctuary. And if I had had any lingering doubts, I discovered when I woke up the next morning that the 'impact' from the night before had actually blown all three gaskets off the back of the guest bathroom toilet! I was standing in water as I stared back at the mystified plumber.

"I don't know *how* on earth all three of these could possibly have blown out at the same time," he mumbled. Needless to say, I wasn't about to try to explain it to him. I did, however, add house-hunting to my afternoon to-do-list. It was a growing list that also included dealing with some health issues.

I had pushed so hard in supporting the metaphysical students in the last few years that my health was suffering. I couldn't shake the terrible feeling that something wasn't right on a massive planetary-level scale either, and that cascaded one evening to realizations filled with pure, soul-splitting grief. I heard myself saying over and over again to my guides as I came out of meditation, *"Something is wrong. We are not where we are supposed to be!"* I could feel it. Could reach out across the planet and feel a huge chasm between what had been hoped for within the 'plan,' and what had actually transpired.

At the time, I worried that the translation of this might only be personal, but within a few days spirit provided the clarification I needed to survive the grief and realize that what I had actually felt was an initiated 'separation of worlds.' Teachers like myself who had come in with 'the Teams' had held on for an extra three years to try to give as many individual souls the opportunity to transition beyond their negative patterns as possible. Now, it was necessary to bring this to a complete end. Some would need to be left behind by their own choices as the earth and a second group of souls continued to raise their frequencies and move on with their re-patterning into the next stage of energies. For me, this was important to know, but I would still need to take a bit of time to grieve.

Because I was right.

We weren't where we had hoped we'd be at this point. Such a large percentage of humanity still resided in the energetic patterns of negativity, anger, selfishness and war. And this was as clear to see demonstrated by *metaphysicians* being territorial and mean, as it was to watch it played out all the way from corporate offices to the bloodshed in the Middle East. There was absolutely no difference. All of these souls belonged to the same lower-vibrational strata of energy.

I would spend the next months decompressing, re-strengthening and allowing the new elements of my work with Spirit to be revealed in a wonderful new sanctuary and home. My corporate work now supported me with a home office and fun interior design and admin projects. It was clear that spirit was placing me in a safe-zone, completely supported and sequestered away from the bulk of the insanity.

I was aware that this was the beginning of 'the fall' for humanity, in this current time of transition.

We had been here before in the 'experiment' of souls traversing the earth plane. And that part of my recall, lessons and preparation were just beginning. That job as Ambassador was quite possibly about to move from classroom to public view.

Understanding of Purpose

Through some of the difficult moments and upon life-review you had to know that I would be asking spirit the all-important question...What is the *purpose* of this lifetime? I had done and seen incredible things from both a human and non-human viewpoint. I had stood at the top of the Rocky Mountains across the continental divide to work with horses; been briefly on a prime-time drama television show; and from my business-world interactions had been named one of *The Top Forty Under 40,* by a leading Business Journal-Magazine for my unique service in both corporate and nonprofit settings. But between these physical-plane adventures and my amazing work with Spirit, there seemed to be a great deal of struggle required. It would take a review of those first 40 years to realize that from within those struggles came the answer to my original question.

1. I was here to give people a chance. Work with other warriors and teachers to give as many souls as possible the chance to change in this final lifetime at the end of a 5,000-year cycle for humanity. If not accomplished in this life, then they would need to start over somewhere else, because the earth and advancing souls would be shifting and progressing with or without them. And this monumental undertaking for me had been done in the trenches at the same time that I was fulfilling my second and third levels of purpose.

2. I was here to use the last of this cycle of energies on the earth plane to 'finish up old business' of my own. I have lived many, many lifetimes here in my agreement to assist with, guide and participate in the experiment and energetic balancing that needed to be completed. Just because I am part of the 'guiding team' doesn't mean I am exempt from the effects of universal law and the required 'karma' that inappropriate decisions can bring. Emersion is emersion. There are influences that can be initiated only from participation within the physical plane itself. Young souls

eager to experience the physical plane become lost in it as they forget who they are and succumb to the illusion. It was my honor and accepted job to come here and play this role, but the first portion of this lifetime included the opportunity to finish my own balancing processes. Before the end of this particular age and cycle of humanity.

3. The third element of my purpose here in this lifetime had been my agreement to take on, in addition to my own, the last of the 'karma' and energetic balancing for the generations of family in my soul group that had come before me. They had passed for the last time out of the physical realm of the earth plane. There are hundreds of them that I am aware of, that didn't have time to return again before the end of this cycle. I agreed to 'walk for them' and ground whatever was unfinished. This way they could truly be free.

Many metaphysicians separate their worlds and aim at a declared 'ultimate goal' of direct teaching to metaphysical students or having some sort of obvious business in the field. This is the human-way of segregating, as if what you *are* and what you can *do* are two separate lives. For me, I would come to truly understand that metaphysics wasn't to be put in a closet while I dealt with every-day life, nor was it necessary for it to be a *visible* work-product.

When I stood in Corporate America I wrote newsletters, marketing plans and designed communication programs for over 3000 people that guided in how caring for each other was linked to expanding profit margins, and in the subtext worked to lead them in the hopes that they would stop hurting each other out of fear or greed. I weaved universal law directly into the mechanics so that it was hidden in corporate-speak but deliverable should anyone decide to take the higher path. Service to all without sacrifice was presented as a soul test to anyone who touched these opportunities. And this included the 'Non-profits.' For them, I built programs that called them on their own set of inappropriate falsehoods. You don't take money from someone without reciprocation, and there is *always* a way to build actual benefits into programs so that even the donors receive in the circle of giving. This suggestion is actually a far-cry from the way Non-profits currently function, as they demand handouts based on guilt or declared worthiness based on purpose.

In child Protective Services I presented such soul-level opportunities at every level as well, from private-sector leaders to law enforcement to abusive parents. Opportunities to change at both personal and system-wide levels were offered. And all the while, I was caring for and holding in my arms beaten children, some as young as three years old with the pain in their eyes from being raped by a father or thrown away like garbage by their mother. I used healing tools and called on guides and even other practitioners from halfway around the world on occasion to assist with especially difficult cases for soul recovery and extraction.

And finally, when I sat as a direct instructor in metaphysics, I realized that this was not any sort of 'ultimate' practitioner method of delivery. If anything, it was the minute-by-minute street-work done under pressure that was larger and of greatest importance. This is a point that I hope allows you to unite all parts of your life and abilities, and helps you see the opportunities that are presented to you here in this monumental final lifetime before the turning of an age of humanity.

Practitioner's Guide

Practitioner's Guide

In the pages that follow, you will find an in-depth *Practitioner's Guide* to assist you on your own path. This Guide includes information on a variety of subjects that can be used to build your personal 'toolbox' and open further your communication gateways and abilities in working with spirit. These include:

- ❖ Discussions on manifestation, what the end of this age of humanity brings and how to prepare for and navigate the earth changes
- ❖ Understanding and dealing with 'sensitivities'
- ❖ Mastery-work exercises to expand intuitive abilities and personal spirit guide communication
- ❖ An at-Home Study Guide for practitioners who wish to increase their metaphysical knowledge base in astrology, mediumship, universal law, etc.
- ❖ Select direct Spirit-channelings to assist practitioners

Mastery Work Exercises in this book are defined as serious 'interactives' for practitioners dedicated to building their mastery in working directly with Spirit through exercises that can be done at home. Your Guides are always present to work directly with you whether you are in a classroom setting or dropping into altered state in privacy. There are powerful energies available to work with now, and we hope that you will dedicate yourself daily to interacting with them. These suggested path-work exercises and tools provide a method of entry into your next level of mastery. We have entered a time where practitioners will begin to realize that crossing over into multiple areas of metaphysical practice will greatly enhance their personal communication gateways and ability to serve. So you will constantly notice our dedication to providing access to a variety of study and connection options that also are designed to help you step into your power and become self-sufficient. You can't just read about things and work only from an intellectual standpoint. You must step into the energies and *work* with them to advance.

****

The Factors
Coping with the Energies of the Planetary Transition

In 2007 when we first started to add 'Dealing Daily with Sensitivity Issues' to our classroom programs, it was met with polite interest and students squirming in their chairs waiting to get to the more exciting mediumship portion of the training. That soon changed to receiving direct requests for assistance in coping with the pain and discomfort that intuitives/sensitives are facing in their daily lives due to the monumental energetic shifts occurring for them, the planet, humanity and those they must interact with each day.

What Seemed Unimportant Is Now A Necessity
Though we can certainly identify with, and are sorry to hear when someone is having sensitivity issues, we are equally thrilled because it means their abilities are expanding and becoming stronger on the positive side of in-the-moment communication with Spirit. This is a sign that they are beginning to relax into self acceptance and into allowing those communication gateways to be more on-line and open. Unfortunately, as many of you are experiencing, this comes with the difficulty of being overwhelmed by so many things that used to be simple. So to put this into perspective, it's important to understand the mountain of factors contributing to the transition effects and how you might be feeling blind-sided by them.

Understanding the Factors
We are now having to deal daily with the speed-up of time, the energetic shifts of both light and darkness (fear) as this incredible rebalancing is occurring. The next section (2012 & The

Mayan Calendar) provides additional information to help you better understand this. And it is not just humanity on this plane of existence that is shifting, but also across multiple dimensions, with the earth working through her own evolution as well. Add this to your personal clearing, which as a more consciously-living soul during this time you have most likely called on an acceleration of experiences in the last 10-20 years. Many are seeing their personal issues reaching a climax now, and WOW ...is it any wonder why the old metaphysical thought process of... *just surround yourself with a light bubble and nothing will feel bad...* might not be quite as effective these days...?! We are sharing these larger view concepts with you first, so that you can see that it will now simply be a day-by-day, hour-by-hour process of fine-tuning your own intuitive awareness and dedication to keeping a clear channel of communication open with your guides so that you can literally move yourself physically to a better location in an instant. And we want you to understand that it's ok to do just that. Rooms, situations, entertainment options and relationships that once were fun or normal, may now be painful. And at first, you will cycle through questioning and judging yourself

... Shouldn't I be able to control this...?
... I'm sad because all the things that used to be fun aren't anymore...so what's left for me...?

You will find that the list of people who are given access to spend time with you gets shorter and shorter because you have energetically evolved beyond their dramas, beliefs, decisions and choices. Watching them in a room becomes a surreal experience similar to watching a bad movie that no longer makes any sense to you. Many people are now being forced to deal with their issues, and if they fight it, they may end up lashing out at you. This leads to another round of sadness and feelings of loss and confusion.

But let's put it into a different light. The key now is to face your own issues with gentle honesty on an ongoing basis and surrender to any intuitional guidance that instructs you to physically step out of a room. This change is sending many of us into a pattern that encourages us to be more hermit-like and step away from the world at the moment; while the storms rage through the lives of others and across the planet. We hope you will view this as just the next evolutionary step needed during the shedding process, and understand that it is better to flow *with* the river than fight the current.

2012 & the Mayan Calendar

If you've been feeling like there is something important going on these days, but can't quite put your finger on what it is, we thought we would take a moment to provide you with a few interesting facts.

It is believed that the Mayan Calendar is an "Evolutionary Timeline" that very specifically tracks the cycles and evolution of humanity. We aren't going to get into the detailed math of how it breaks down, but we will tell you that it is a timeline of 5,125 years of history called the "Long Count" that ranges from 3115 BC to October 28, 2011. Broken down into segments, time itself accelerates x20 at the interval marks.

The last big x20 speedup of time occurred in 1998/1999...which is why just about everyone you know keeps commenting about how time seems to be going by so fast. It's noticeable now to even the non-metaphysicians. It feels like we are stuck on a carnival ride or inside a centrifuge, plastered against the wall as it spins at incredible speeds!

You may have noticed that the end date of the Mayan Calendar we note above is before 2012. This is because the sacred calendars on earth have an agreement that the year be counted as 360 days rather than 365 for this evolutionary timeline exercise. This includes the Dynastic Egyptians, the Mesoamericans such as the Mayans, Incans, etc., and the Vedic Culture of India. These cultures additionally used the 365 day calendar as a physical and agricultural one to plant crops, but not for marking sacred time.

In addition to the ancient cultures being in agreement, a miraculous thing has happened in just the last 50 years...the scientific community of astronomers and archeologists have also come into agreement with the metaphysical community findings.

This is HUGE considering they rarely allow the acknowledgment of common ground. But recent scientific findings and archeological digs have given them the "proof" they require to jump on board.

Another area of factual alignment is the discovery in the arctic circle (due to melting), of a layer that provides proof of a cataclysm on earth around the time period of 11,500 BC. It is believed that this was caused by a supernova fragment from the Velas System hitting earth. Native American cultures call this the time when the earth almost died, and it brought an end to the advanced cultures that resided on the planet. It did, in fact, cause such trauma to humanity that it also has been suggested that this survival period was the cause of humanity's regression to violence and a distrust of nature. Today this is evident in the way we do not live or reside in harmony with the elements and earth, and our disrespect for life.

So why did it occur and what does the "end" of the ancient calendars mean? Turning our eyes away from disaster scenarios and toward the positive potential inherent in such a monumentally important time period, we also want to point out something amazing that occurred as a result of the Velas Supernova collision. After impact, the tectonic plates separated on the planet into a very specific (and scientifically agreed upon) number. Native Americans call the earth "Turtle Island" because it now matches the proportions of the pattern of the shell of a turtle. This also happens to have turned the earth into a perfect icosahedron in alignment with sacred geometry!

It should always be remembered that the earth has its own destiny and life plan, and perhaps it is time to both consciously recognize the past trauma as the cause of our mistrust, as well as allowing it to fade. It's very possible that the earth is actually finishing up with a 'settling down' period from its own evolution. Rather than a disastrous outcome, a pole shift may be on the schedule to bring everything back into alignment after the impact left the earth tilting in 11,500BC. (Hint: the majority of other planets don't tilt).

And as for what the next 3-4 years brings, we encourage you to remember that your personal experience will be in alignment with your soul plan, and not entirely at the mercy of prevailing winds. We encourage more strongly than ever that attunement and alignment with Spirit and your own internal guidance link to your higher self become your number one priority now daily. The last 360 day segment on the Mayan Calendar that leads up to October 28, 2011 will initiate another x20 speed up of time! So if you think you can feel it now, wait until we hit that last cycle! We will have worked through the National and Planetary, and then be standing in what the Mayans call the final Galactic Underworld cycle. The previous time periods saw the world shift through nationalism to where we are now feeling like a planetary community. Advancements in communication delineate this very visually. In just the last 50 years we have gone from carrier postal mail to cell phones and computers! In this final segment it is suggested that we have the opportunity to advance to the point of again using our whole brain and more of our DNA in communication. It is also hoped that a turn may occur in a large percentage of the masses toward less violence and more eco-centered options for working in harmony with the planet. And being that this is a "galactic" period, perhaps the "quarantine" placed on earth might be lifted as well if we can achieve some of these goals.

****** Direct Channeling from Spirit ******

Understanding the "Access Point" Available in a Consciousness Convergence

We came upon the turning of another visible measure of time as we entered the month of July, and much excitement was building for what was being called the Consciousness Convergence of July 17-18, 2010. We are always pleased when large groups of people find a common focal point in positive thoughts of love, harmony and the potential for raising the planetary vibration. This type of focus can have wonderful effect, but we wanted to redirect you to a reminder of the purpose of such an occurrence. Many become so externally focused that there is a lingering disappointment as the date of such an 'event' comes and goes. This is because the 'high' that is chased must always be followed by a 'low' if the event is not held simply as a point of peace. The pendulum of excitement and anticipation can be fun and a wonderful access to joy, but should be a time that is used to relax into the energies without preconception of an outcome. We encourage you as you acknowledge or participate in such an event to feel how the rhythm of the universe is being personalized for YOU in addition to what effect it may have on humanity.

The announcement of 'windows' in the universe of available alignment and energy provide opportunity for humanity, but should be used and applied personally and within. You are not waiting for one convergence that will rule them all or bring some sort of instantaneous enlightenment. Enlightenment is an 'unfoldment' and progression of steps, just like the earth changes you see heightening in an ebb and flow all around you now. Your job is to heighten your intuitive skills and learn to flow with the highest vibrations available in every moment. There is no event outside of you that will occur to 'fix' anything. But there are events, changes and energies gifted that bring support and opportunity. We frequently remind the medium..."Your path is your own." ...when she feels torn about not having the same experiences as others, or in accordance with a grand declaration of astrology or cultural occurrence. She then shifts back to peace and becomes again aware of how appropriate is the uniqueness of her personal path. And this is true for every soul.

Please keep in mind that we are not saying you are 'exempt' from the occurrences in the world around you... just reminding you that there is much you can do about your own situations by realizing that detachment and peace are always an option you can claim; and maintaining this state should be one of your highest priorities. Windows of convergence, alignment and opportunity do not just arrive with massive planetary shifts. They can be accessed at the

*turning of the month, year, your birthday, and especially arrive
when you make a personal soul-level decision or change on the
internal planes that you set forth to initiate on the physical plane.
It should be wonderful news to you that though there are things
that may come and go on the earth plane, your personal soul
growth and advancement is not at the mercy of the prevailing
patterns and choices of humanity. Take a deep breath and feel the
freedom available to you. Only your own decisions determine that.
Find the peaceful flow-point of the path you are currently on, and
use dates and events you FEEL apply to you personally.*

****

Understanding Nature's New Struggle

For most sensitives, connecting with the elements of nature
has always been a true sanctuary, but this too is changing as the
earth reacts to abuse and continues her own decision-making and
life cycle. The sun is twenty times more powerful and painful in
its rays than it was in the 1980s. Energy blasts from the universe
are crashing into the planet to assist with the transformation, but it
is a seriously intense and wild ride. Humanity is filled with fear
and anger and these energies too, are rolling across the planet,
literally at war with itself. This is coming to a climax with the end
of a 3000+ year AGE of all humanity ending shortly (2011 is the
actual Mayan calendar end date). In light of all of this, it becomes
completely understandable that some days your internal guidance
system or Guides will say... T*oday you rest. Today is not a good
day to be outside.* Though we love nature, soft and supportive
energies are not all that we are hit with these days when we sit by
the lake or walk in the garden.

Primary Focus for Interaction

We all have responsibilities that include going to work,
school, the grocery store, etc. Surrender to the exercise of putting
guidance first so that you will *feel* the best times to go out, and
then let support flow to you. When you stand somewhere that is
uncomfortable, focus on the strength that flows through you and

radiates outward rather than trying to withdraw your energy field from the touch of something painful. Withdrawal alone only serves through negative/fear intent to drag the discomfort closer to you.

Health Issues & Our Participation

We have noticed an increase in health issues for many of the intuitives and sensitives we work with. Our sensitive abilities can make us more susceptible to energy impacts, which in turn can make us physically ill. It is also occurring to many that humanity may not reach some perfect shift into a garden-of-eden-state by 2012, and we are processing the worlds grief as well as contemplating what this means to our personal missions here at the soul level, and what role we should play in it all. It is important to remember that the quest for personal peace contributes energetically to the positive transformation underway, no matter what humanity chooses. And there may be times when having a very public method for assisting might not be the path you expected.

We encourage you to consider that taking care of yourself is of greatest importance now so that you will be available when the universe does send someone to your doorstep. Or that perhaps what is truly needed from you is on an energetic level more than a direct interaction. Now is the time to use your training and tools in a realistic, and possibly new, daily methodology. To surrender to whatever your intuition is telling you to do even if this time in your life is not what you expected it would be. Create new supportive play-time things you can do in more protected sanctuaries to support yourself. View what is happening with as much satisfaction as you can muster, knowing that you are one of very few consciously awakened souls on the planet graced to be aware of the bigger picture, rather than having to suffer like those who don't understand what is happening.

The Four Prime Directives for Practitioners

Rarely do I seem to be called upon to deliver "fluffy" metaphysics or messages in my travels, and as we enter into a time of momentous change, this trend continues with information from spirit that speaks practical truth while assuring support through transition. (4) prime directives have been outlined, which we strongly encourage all metaphysical practitioners to follow; as time is now short for humanity to shift. The definition of a *practitioner*, as outlined to us, is anyone who uses metaphysical tools and techniques for personal objectives or professional service. These guidelines will lay the foundation for a new methodology in metaphysical study and practice for those who embrace this next evolutionary step. Many speak of the path to ascension, and we embrace the concept as the evolutionary steps each soul takes on the journey to demonstrating grace, love and truth in every interaction. It isn't a magical destination to be suddenly and surprisingly granted as the end of this recorded age occurs in 2011-2012, but instead it is come to gradually through decisions made in the accessing and delivery of creation itself through the soul.

1. Remove the "lines" that separate the various methods and metaphysical practices of healing, mediumship, shamanism, meditation, channeling, and others. Allow a merger and amplification of the "communication gateways" with spirit. Many schools and courses insist on the use of only one system or methodology of practice and this mentality is hindering practitioners and students from accessing and maximizing their abilities and work. The human methods in society praise single-subject study focus, but the time has come to recognize the potential barriers to expansion inherent in this. In truth, the more diverse and open-minded the course of study, the more effective practitioners will be from this point forward. The key now is to fine tune each practitioners internal guidance system so that negative or inaccurate methods can quickly be rejected and stepped away from in exchange for accurate and powerful tools and techniques that are in alignment with the practitioners highest path and purpose. There are many races and beings both on and off planet that are available to work with should the choice be made to embrace the multitude of methods, tools and access points rather than focusing only on a single technique. Practitioners and students are encouraged to notice when fear and control issues are the driving force behind any interaction.

2. Break free from the habit of sectioning off metaphysics separate from daily interactions, and begin to walk as Spirit-connected first and human second. This does not have to be publicly revealed, it is simply a dedication to daily quiet focus allowed to expand so that Guides and helpers can communicate more freely with you on all topics including the mundane ones in-the-moment. Remember you will only feel the support of your nonphysical team more frequently when you begin to allow them to function as one at your side. They are waiting and ready to do so when you reach for them and embrace the potential of this new relationship level.

3. Remove all territorial behaviors and walk-your-talk in elevated service to humanity. Many metaphysical practitioners and communities have precipitated negative human behaviors and follow practices that act as if competition is an actual reality. On the higher planes, it is non existent, and we encourage all metaphysical teachers and practitioners to take the next step in their commitment to humanity by walking as a living example in the world, one that does not tolerate speaking negatively of others or territorial behaviors. What will be built in the next few years to support the collective whole will largely depend on the death of this dichotomy in each practitioner, instructor and metaphysical learning center.

4. Speak truth to any person, student or practitioner in your realm that it is no longer acceptable for metaphysical circles to perpetuate the drama of victimhood cycles. Create new circles for those who understand this and have no desire to use metaphysics as a crutch, but instead can be observed to allow a clearing of any issue that arises without a return to it for the sake of demanding love and attention. This does not mean that occasionally a different layer of some past issue may appear for the next stage of healing and release to be done, but none of it will be used for ongoing dramatics.

****** **Direct Channeling from Spirit** ******

Personal Shiftings Effect on the Whole & the Mayan Calendar
As time marches on, the Mayan calendar shows creation of the universe is conducted in 9 waves. (Nine in numerology being the number of completion, endings and awakened consciousness.) But people forget that what is available for creation and realization is determined by individual choice and implemented change. Not simply brought about by the delivery of outside energy or forces. It is the energy provided through the universe and evolved beings working in concert that puts forth the intention to support transformation, but it in no way guarantees it. It is not simply the marching on of a calendar that determines the final outcome, and you are not waiting on delivery of an evolved time from the universe. The universe is waiting on you. And the determination of evolution does trickle down to this individual level where most live in denial.

What would you change in your life and your own personal behaviors if we told you that your place in the new world would be in large part determined by your participation decisions at the personal level and whether you end or modify any relationship that involves abuse at any level (verbal, mental, emotional, physical). There is no gray area. There is only truth of intentions and your participation in it. This is what we call your "jurisdiction" and area of personal responsibility for which your soul is held responsible. There is a time to say "no," "enough" and speak truth to those in your care that forces a confrontation so that truth is offered. Who will do it if not you who can see through the illusion...?

You are responsible for standing in your own power and halting any negative behavior inflicted upon yourself as well. Behind closed doors this may include the participation and choice to have addictions to food, smoking, etc. It may be subversive abuse on yourself in the form of pushing to exhaustion for approval from others, not cleaning up your living space (addiction to chaos over order and peace), and not sitting to meditate regularly and declaring "but for some reason I have resistance." These are all choices to follow negative personal patterns rather than allowing the evolution of your soul. Many metaphysical practitioners 'hide' in the assistance of helping others as part of the excuse and pattern of getting out of dealing with their own issues. Sharing your love and light through conscious intention at the community and global level is of great assistance, but when you look in the mirror today, ask yourself how much you personally are assisting in the upliftment of humanity by doing the thing most frightening, yet easiest and within your control... calling a total halt to your own personal, learned, negative behavior patterns.

If you are still embroiled in struggle with others, ask yourself why you choose to continue to do so. So you think there is an obligation because they are "family" or long time "friends"...? Do you stay out of fear of being alone or to avoid pain? Do you not see that taking the high road means being the one to walk away from any conversation or relationship, to display for them what higher love truly looks like? If participation equals support of inappropriate behavior patterns, then that is the least supportive choice you can make at the soul level for them and for yourself. Is it not better that you walk as an example of how souls stepping into the new energy and time of awakening should behave...? You may be met with vicious anger, a suggestion that you feel guilty, and worsening of behavior from those people who want no part of change yet wish to keep you involved in their negativity so they can "feed" off of you and the situation, but you will have elevated your own soul, the energy of the planet and made a space for any who wish to be brave and leave their negative patterns behind to follow if you walk away. This is the path of a Light Worker. This is the choice the true Teachers make as they stand on the rim and are the first wave to assist this planet and humanity in the hopes for a positive outcome. You inserted yourself into your current life circumstances to show the humans how to get out of theirs. They would not have believed you if you didn't come through it with them. And we, here, on the other side are so honored by the courage each of you has shown to participate in this way. The next 18 months will determine the true progress of humanity and each of you at the individual soul level. There is no longer years available to relax and deal with these things later. The energies available now will not be available again in this type of convergence on the earth plane. We all have waited hundreds of thousands of years for this chance. We hope that you will use this opportunity as well as your connection to us and our love, to elevate your own souls with the realization that this is the key to the upliftment of humanity.

****

The Persistent Message

We have noticed in the channelings that are now occurring that there is a theme arising with urgency. It is time to put an end to the localized dramas. And if a personality won't do it willingly, then the soul will step in and create a potentially painful scenario to get the person's attention and re-aim them toward the goals set forth for the lifetime. In the past, there was a gentler pace allowed for such things, but that will no longer be the case. This purging of negative patterns is a requirement prior to being given individual access to higher frequencies and communications, and it is a transition completely within each soul's control. Universal Law has always been absolute, but now there is a great collision of energies at play on the world stage with a speeding up of time added to the rebalancing that began in 2008. Action now needs to be taken to build truly supportive structures in the face of false "industries" being ripped down. Who will do it? Will you sit in your little corner of the world and simply watch, or will you pick up an activity within your control and serve now? Will you decide to continue to play in endless relationship dramas and behaviors or will you stop?

****** **Direct Channeling from Spirit** ******

The Energetics of Relationships & Their Endings
As you have all felt the delivery and approach of endings of late, we wish to answer your direct questions on this topic. And many a question has come to mind as you attempt to navigate accelerated changes and the fears they bring.

We first wish to remind you that change is never thrust upon you without your consent. And in truth, it is rarely a surprise. A specific question brought to us was 'how to survive divorce.' The first question to ask yourself, is what was the purpose and your TRUE core intention for entering into the marriage or any other relationship for that matter. We must go back to the beginning to understand the ending and honor our paths with the truths necessary not to repeat the past. It is important to know that there are ONLY two real core intentions that any decision in life is made from. Love or fear. And though there may have been love present, if there was also any fear-based reasons within the decision to unite in relationship, then the pathway and outcome of that relationship must always deliver on that fear. Your soul will not allow any falsehood to stand. And fear is a falsehood. This may have included fear of being alone in the world now or as aging occurs; fear of not being able to pay the bills by yourself; fear of disappointing your parents or not living up to family traditions and obligations; deep self-loathing and fear that you won't find anyone "better" who will love you so you choose to put up with abuse of some kind; etc.

With honor and honesty must you enter, walk within, and eventually leave any relationship. For nothing will remain hidden. It must all be dealt with. So 'surviving' divorce or the ending of any type of relationship will mean being kind, honest and standing in your power and truth whereby you will claim all parts of your soul and allow even the frightened aspects to heal. Sometimes to do this, a clean break and departure is necessary. You will be held accountable for your behavior, and the other soul/personality held responsible for theirs. Any negative treatment, display or pattern will continue to boomerang back in this relationship or the next. You must decide what is truly within you to be claimed, ended, released. This is how you will find actual freedom.

Decisions made in anger, fear, guilt or any reason that is not the loving delivery for all, will have to be experienced later by the individual who inflicts it. Energy out - energy back. Energy only grounds on the person who sends it out. And let us be clear. If you find your truth and choose to walk away because the other personality refuses to face or halt damaging behavior or negative patterns, you will *have made the loving choice for both of you at the soul level to end it. For in experiencing the loss of you, they are given another opportunity to change.*

And finally on this subject, we wish to remind you again that energy is everything. The people we interact with in relationships are energetically linked to us physically, mentally, emotionally, aurically. If angry situations, negative relationships or ongoing negative thoughts are allowed to persist in the life, this is energy you are 'leaking' or may even build into a physical illness. That being said, we ask if it is worth it to hang on to such people and interactions or mentally keep reliving past anger or perceived injustice or hurts...? The universe is perfect justice. Those displaying negative behaviors or attempting to hurt others will later get to experience someone, somewhere doing the same to them. Knowledge of this universal law of ten-fold return can be used to detach at every level and bring peace if you choose to let it.

****

Step into Your Blueprint

The perfect blueprint exists within the auric field and higher self connections for each of you to access once a dedication to soul purpose is made at the next level. It is as simple as a decision, and then requires that you commit to removing yourself from old groups, relationships and situations that you are aware are detrimental or of lower frequency. You may then ask spirit/your guides/the universe to provide a new avenue for you to expand into for study and exploration. It will be provided. We have found that the Pleadian method of a minimum of one teacher for every ten students, and always a clear-channel non-ego-based healer in the room is a very important component that we suggest you seek out should your personal journey lead you to group work. The reason for this is because lifetimes of soul memory are intertwined with the jewels of ability for each student/practitioner, and release of past pain will need to be addressed in-the-moment as each step is taken.

Rebalancing Effects and Their Roots in Our Distant Past

Massive planetary upheaval in the recent past, with the most devastating reported to have occurred in 9500 BC (confirmed by scientific analysis), was followed by two smaller episodes. These were moments imprinted on humanity that created a deep seated fear at many levels especially with regard to our physical safety, and an accompanying distrust and unfortunate detachment from nature. The bible and its stories merge these three occurrences together in the concept of the great flood. No one would disagree that our basic society patterns are built on fear-based beliefs in business, interactions with others and especially survival in a prepare-for-the-worst-mentality. With the majority fixated on a tandem concrete belief system (only acknowledging that the physical dimension and present lifetime are real), it has been very difficult to bring this past life cellular-memory trauma to consciousness for release. So humanity now faces a critical point in history where ecogenocide is very possible. The planet is a living organism that we have pushed to the limit in the past with negative use of technology, and now we must find a harmony with it in order to be able to stay. We will have to recognize the worlds beyond the physical, clear the fear, and find a merger point with nature.

Though we will tell you that many realizations will come to society through pain and discomfort, this does not have to be the case for you as an individual. Your job is to work on the harmonization of your own path and attunement within your own realm, while not allowing yourself to plug into the massive fear-based dramas unfolding across the globe. Your internal guidance system will point the way to your safe haven if you dedicate yourself to strengthening your personal communication gateways as has been suggested. Sit in the eye of the hurricane and ask Spirit what the truth is in any situation you are witness to. It isn't mysterious when looking through metaphysical eyes. People are not as devastatingly without resources as the news media insinuates. A decline in obsessive overproduction and waste is giving way to using what is already in hand. How can a trend back to quality products be forced to occur unless people become unwilling to re-purchase low quality items each year? The automobile industry in the United States turns out thousands of vehicles of low quality and most dealers play at unfair practices to maximize profits at the expense of customers. Few businesses run on a platform of true equality in giving and receiving fairly. So, when we tell you that there will be pain in transformation, we suggest you view it as a necessary adjustment. And this brings us to a discussion about employment.

Our school systems, for the most part are not set up to nurture children. Individual passion, creativity and soul-level talents and abilities do not enter into the picture within the current system of standardized tests and fear for the future. As some people now find themselves no longer employed, we encourage practitioners to guide them to review their life and dreams and choose a new path that is in closer alignment to an awareness of joy and true purpose. This rebalancing is an encouragement to step away from jobs or companies that were unsupportive for them or others. They are brought to this point of pain as a soul-level induced opportunity for a life-review. (Remember we mentioned that the soul will take matters into its own hands if the personality is unwilling to make changes on its own.)

Holding a viewpoint based in truth and not judgment, labels or fear will be one of the most important jobs for each practitioner now. This is the equivalent to holding the light and will need to be done in each situation and room you will be called into. We also mentioned that there should be no separation between metaphysical rooms and everyday rooms. This is what we meant. Political, geographic, economic, racial and socioeconomic labels and categories people place themselves and others into create blockages to solutions. It becomes a self-imposed destructive wheel of manifestation. Teach people to see and follow higher truth without accusation and you will go to sleep each night knowing you have served to tip the balance of planetary energy in a positive direction.

******* **Direct Channeling from Spirit** ******

Upcoming Mayan Galactic Alignments & Your Place in It
It is all about perspective isn't it...? From the small segment of this life that you pursue and know on a daily basis, you make decisions, assumptions and either consciously or subconsciously choose to plug into certain societal and mass consciousness beliefs and waves of participation. This is the time of the choosing, above all else. Make no mistake that the cycle portrayed and definitions that come forth from the reading of the Mayan calendars, speak of end times that will certainly be followed by the opportunity for new beginnings. There have been civilizations that have come to an end and transition such as Atlantis and Lemuria, the Mayan Empire and so many others in the cyclical pattern of choice and intervention. This is not a reason to hold personal fear, but instead a time to expand your consciousness to a galactic one, which can bring you peace, understanding and connection to us that uplifts your personal world. You manifest what you focus on, and we would warn you to stop and take a look at how you spend your days. You need not be Mother Teresa to allow for dramatic higher

connections in your daily life, but you do need to remember that if your 'career' and personal interactions with others are of war, impatience, judgment, negativity, anger and following of negative patterns of behavior, then perhaps a life and soul review is in order. Do you contribute in your work to the upliftment of humanity or the perpetuation of planetary destruction and harm...? What products, industries and organizations to you support through your employment, purchasing and time...?

From the perspective of the Mayans, time is cyclical. All things follow a circle. When one cycle of time ends, another begins. What the Mayans saw and predicted for our lifetime is a very large end point in a very long cycle, with its manifestations to be determined by the energetic state of humanity. They have proven to be correct that this is a profound time of change when humanity will be forced to face itself and make new decisions about how they treat each other, the planet and other life forms. How this affects you, personally, will be determined by your level of evolution and choices you have made to either follow your soul's higher path in daily decision-making, life-decisions and core choices or not.

.

✳✳

Practitioner's Guide to the Galaxy

This planet has long been a focal point for an attempt at creation through DNA evolution as well as a place for individual souls to experience individual creation. As far back as 300 billion years ago the storyline includes the rise of civilizations both isolated and interactive with other planetary races, and many agendas have been played out with both success and failure. At this point in history, there is a combination of great enthusiasm for the potential that exists as well as a solemn dedication to duty built into many of us who have awareness of what is occurring. This awareness includes knowledge that some of us were sent in as "The Teams" (to use a bit of Navy Seal military terminology). We are positioned to stand as watchtowers, teachers, sentinels and warriors. We carry a nearly unwavering intensity of purpose that insists on truth over popularity, and we accept that our jobs are nonphysically linked together with others of our kind, translated frequently in a behind-the-scenes capacity. This is more powerful than an ego-filled individual could imagine. If this definition applies to you, then everything that has been said here will resonate with you in absolution.

From this standpoint, we can tell you that a great battle is occurring at this time in plain sight for control of the planet and masses. As the bible was used by the Catholic Church to infuse control while simultaneously hiding the mechanics of individual creation through the Universal Laws; governments and wealthy factions also continue to apply their own pressure across the globe. Earth has been in a quarantined status for some time from other races on a mass consciousness scale due to these issues and humanity's willingness to do harm without respect or compassion. We ask of each practitioner to not dwell on this grand scale of issues to the detriment of your human viewpoint. Such great waves of fear and anger will be sweeping the planet that there will be days when just the act of walking out your front door will cause you great discomfort. As you have worked to strengthen your communication with Spirit, and removed negative influences and relationships, we now encourage you to define your personal homes with amplified purpose and attention paid to making them a sanctuary. Allow divine order to speak to you. Release objects that carry old energy that no longer reflects your new pattern. Simplify your surroundings and invite helpers such as crystals, aromatherapy with pure essential oils, and plants to grace your environment. This will broadcast into the universe as a declaration to attract peace and prosperity, as well as put forth the invitation to Spirit to work with you at a deeper level. Keep in mind that you are not waiting to hear from them what is to be done, *they* are waiting for *you* to choose to amplify your ability as a clear channel without ego, negativity or other blockages. Many practitioners will experience great challenges if they have not dealt with ego issues, removal of negative behavior patterns or if their practices are not in alignment with highest truth. Others will realize how far they have come in obtaining the equivalent of their master's degree on planet earth. Just as humanity will be halted from hurting other planets, races and even the earth itself, this will be a testing period for anyone not functioning from higher energies or intentions. We call this the granting of grace through realization.

****

Building Your Abilities with at-Home Study

Building Your Abilities with at-Home Study

For those of you who are interested in enhancing your own abilities in intuition, mediumship and more, we provide this at-home study guide. It contains book recommendations, exercises to practice, tools and techniques that intertwine and allow expansion. We have found that many students who work in metaphysics and attend classes do so for the "high," but few have a dedication and understanding that daily practices and multi-subject exploration are the key. We hope you will meditate and work with some practitioner method each day so that you can enjoy benefits and growth beyond the formal classroom. You may also use the *Mastery Work* exercises provided, that provide very specific techniques and exercises for you to explore and use.

Communicating with Spirit
No matter your specific belief system, most people in search of self-transformation on a spiritual level have accepted that there is more out there than can be seen with the physical eyes. Coincidences and synchronicity are noticed and often unexplainable in the context of normal living. It is at this point that many focus on the possibility of finding a method of communication to their higher self, God, intuition, their soul, or non-physical entities we call Guides. Acknowledging something larger is an excellent step, and we encourage students to follow the path most comfortable to them as they move forward to the next level...developing a method and language.

Communication directly with Spirit (our term for any non-physical being & working beyond the physical), isn't as complicated as people think. Intuition is a tool that all of us were born with, and Spirit actually draws on an individual's personal experiences to develop a vocabulary. The universe/God/Guides/your higher self is standing-by to answer, as soon as an individual reaches out to communicate, and *symbol* is the highest form of communication in the universe. These symbols can come in the form of animals, numbers, objects, etc.

Everything has a specific vibration and energy, and studying these with the conscious intention of using them as a communication tool will heighten intuitional abilities. Similar to an athlete or musician who must practice, metaphysical practitioners will have to practice using their intuitional muscles to increase skill and accuracy. Far from requiring blind faith; using kinesiology, divination systems and directed physical applications can bring interactions with Spirit into the physical arena where proof comes from initiating contact and watching results. Everything we recommend has a physical exercise for students to experience direct results if applied. These tools then become useful in daily living and decision-making, and that can ease the fear of the unknown...making life a bit easier to manage.

How does this help with increasing psychic ability....?

Everyone is born with the ability to use their intuition. Some people are visual and often see images flash in their minds. This is how *clairvoyance* works, and with focused intention can be a direct method of communication rather than random. Those who are more feeling-based are termed to be *clairsentient*. You have experienced this yourself if you've even had a *feeling* about something and it turned out to be true. Beyond learning these simple definitions, using intuition to communicate and receive information becomes a simple exercise in building your personal vocabulary, asking the universe and then paying attention to occurrences and impressions. In truth, this ability has always been there, but society doesn't provide the training to children to use it. A high-functioning intuitive will use these and constantly be paying attention to images popping into their head, feelings and knowingness in-the-moment to read people and situations. This can allow for quick and accurate decision-making.

So if you're ready to start building bridges, a personal vocabulary and applying these things for yourself, here are some recommendations...

Numerology and the Communication of Numbers

Numbers are everywhere. (Bank accounts, addresses, dates, etc.) Nearly everything in the world is associated with a number of some kind, and this gives us a serious clue to the vibration and meaning attached to it. *Numerology and The Divine Triangle*, is one of our favorite reference books, and we highly recommend having it on your shelf. It provides the vibrational information for every number including specific correlation with astrological influences and tarot up to 78. Though we are not specifically recommending this book for its numerological method of personal forecasting, it gives you an all-inclusive reference manual for simple reduction and instant application. For example, take any number (like your home address) and add the individual numbers together. If you live at 1328 Maplecrest Drive, you would add $1+3+2+8 = 14$. Reduce any number in this way until you reach a number between 1 and 78, then look in this excellent guide to see what the vibration is. We have found in the last 15 years of working with numerology that it has astounding accuracy for telling you what type of occurrences will be drawn to an address (and the people living there), bank account, etc. This methodology has been in use for thousands of years and understanding the basic numbers 1-9 will give you a piece of your new working vocabulary.

Divination Systems

Divination Systems such as Tarot cards, Animal Medicine Cards, Angel Cards or others can be an excellent bridge to work directly with your higher self/Spirit. Legend and religion have often branded this methodology in a negative way, but in truth, they are just a communication tool for use or abuse depending on how a person chooses to behave when using them. Again, there is a strong use of symbol attached to meaning in any card system, and this is the important focus for linking them with intuition-building. The second reason we recommend them is for the assistance they can provide thanks to *The Law of Attraction*. This is one of the guiding principles of Universal Law, which is the actual 'rule book' for how and why things occur and manifest on all planes of existence. When working with cards, this translates to… ask a question…focus your intention on something…and the law of attraction delivers the answer vibrationally in the form of specific cards. The cards drawn are not random accidents. People who use them are always amazed at how appropriate and specific the answers are, and when multiple types of decks are used at the same time, often the cards pulled from each are nearly duplicates. This is a fascinating and fun way to learn to listen and build your intuitional muscles.

Working with Tarot

Though there is a wide array of Tarot decks to choose from, we recommend the Rider-Waite Tarot as a primary system combined with using *A Magical Course in Tarot* by Michele Morgan, as a translation manual. We are aware that this deck contains the most intact and accurate symbology from the ancient lineage of the mystery schools (rather than fancy new age modern art). It is said that when metaphysical practitioners thousands of years ago foresaw the coming of the dark ages and burning of the library at Alexandria, artists set forth to create these cards to contain the knowledge needed to traverse the life-lessons of earth school. Each of the major arcana cards represents one of these lessons. The symbols carry meaning that will translate subconsciously, and as you progress in your use you will become aware of the actual consciousness of each card. Many people don't realize that even regular playing cards are the mirror of this ancient system. As a serious undertaking, with often stark imagery, we find that Michele Morgan's book is the most exceptional on the market for eliminating the fear and heightening clairsentience and clairvoyance. She makes learning the cards enjoyable and easy to remember. From a practitioner's standpoint, it is very important to note that cards should always be purchased new and primarily handled by a single user. This is because they bond with an individual energetically as they are worked with.

Once you have a solid foundation in the ancient tarot, you can then expand to using and exploring the energies of other decks, styles and artists. On some occasions, new practitioners who are afraid of the ancient tarot may choose to start their communications with angel card decks, fairies, or other softer methods. There is nothing wrong with this. It is important to chart your own path and follow your spirit beyond anyone's recommendation.

If you have an affinity for Native American culture, one of the most conversational alternate divination systems we frequently use are Jaime Sam's *Sacred Path Cards*. Though based in Native American tradition, these cards point the way for in-the-moment decision-making and Spirit communication when used because of the way they are set-up. Simple terminology such as retreat, advance, etc. provides plain language added to symbology to continue building your own vocabulary and communication pathways.

Working with Animal Energy

The animals that walk the earth with us honor our path each time they share their lives and energies. Just as each person has a soul-purpose, each animal has a collective consciousness and vibrational meaning and energy they hold. They are growing in consciousness just as we are, and came to the earth plane to participate. As learning numerology and numbers provides vibrational clues, learning animal energies can add to your vocabulary in communicating with the universe too. Ted Andrews has (2) fantastic reference books that we recommend be added to your book shelf. *Animal-Speak* is the primary guide, and *Animal-Wise* the secondary for more unusual types of animals. It is said in Native American tradition that each person has (9) primary animal guides or totem animals that "walk" with them. These animals often appear physically to that person, but all animal encounters have meaning. Using these reference guides will allow you to apply this meaning and communication from Spirit in-the-moment to understand the messages provided.

****** **Direct Channeling from Spirit** ******

Working Thru the Internal Gates
Much is spoken about "the gates" on this planet. Some of you have deep memory of their use. You call them star gates thru which

inter-dimensional travel is possible. But you forget that in your immersion in this biosphere (earth plane), that the primary gate is within you.

As Practitioners you have been brought to this crossroads of time and spatial reality with the ability to transcend it through an array of specific tools gifted you. Whether your skill set includes shamanistic tendencies to merge with the animals or crossover energetics with the earth itself. Now is the time when you are each responsible for completing your own internal grid and aligning it between "heaven and earth" as they say.

It feels like you are standing out on a ledge since the separation of worlds in August 2009. But this vacuum in a life is scheduled for each to embrace their mastery. Merger with your truest deepest abilities is now possible to transcend the mundane of the daily. To merge with your nonphysical allies in a battle long fought and now at a unique completion point that allows you some time to rest. Embrace it. We stand with you. Release the past and your mourning for those left behind. You must set your eyes now to the rebuilding of your own fields - both energetic and physical. What comes for the humans of the earth plane will now come to pass. Don't count yourself among them. Stand peacefully apart as a master does and use your internal gate for constant access to a peace-making for yourself that you've rarely allowed or acknowledged while immersed in service. This will be needed. Feel the union on a moment by moment merge. Begin to realize the gate that you are. Detach from it all for awhile and feed yourself. No doubt, no pain. Just rulership of your self even as the elements, planets, numbers and celestial entities command rulership of their own energies.

The Chilean earthquake in 2009 was the first, and caused a shift of the earth's axis. This can be scientifically verified through the public NASA reports. The planet is now spinning tighter and faster.

What will come in the manner of earth changes will be a

continuing cascade effect. This is why for those of you tuned in, there is understanding when we say - the classrooms for you are over. Metaphysical classrooms are dissolving and breaking apart as those walking with higher mastery know they can't return to groups playing out continuing human dramas within old settings. Your place is not with them anymore, but instead with us (Spirit). Direct connect now just IS, but leaves you feeling disconnected or detached from your physical life even as you walk thru it. Don't be frightened by this. Embrace it. There is great peace available within it. Allow it to comfort and protect you. Meditate daily as one of your most important tasks. This will build your new alignment and connect you to us, each other, and the future. The loneliness, though you may now stand more physically alone than ever before, isn't real. Connect to your guides and live fully with us, equally sharing your world. These are the days you've trained for.

****** **Mastery Work Exercise** ******

Shaman's Walk
This exercise is designed to show you an access point through the merger of multiple metaphysical disciplines and your personal abilities…a way to step through your inter-dimensional, internal 'gate.' No more is it practical to study just one course like mediumship or shamanism and think that these are meant to stand alone in use. In truth, your personal abilities span far beyond this human concept and with lightning speed spirit can speak to you by using your clairvoyance, clairsentience, psychic, mediumistic and shamanistic abilities nearly all at once. This next octave of mastery and merger is accessible to you through simple application and solo practice working directly with your guides. You don't need to find a classroom or outside instructor to accomplish it.

What you will need for this exercise:
- Favorite music on a portable player - action oriented - good/faster beat - uplifting lyrics

- A place to walk that's got more nature, less people and is in a safe area. Don't walk too close to buildings or in a place where you have to constantly check traffic, etc. You need a safe uninterrupted walking path or track.
- Protective clothing and sunscreen - pay attention to the elements and select a day and time to do this when the outside conditions and energies are supportive and more favorable, rather than assaulting and combative.

How to Engage:

The point of this exercise is to allow the beat of the music synchronized with deliberately paced rhythmic power-walking to set the stage for merger with your guides. This is a faster-paced walk with deep breathing.

- Begin to walk and align and connect with the music.
- Reach with your energies through intention to first connect your spirit and power, to the power that you have the greatest affinity for. (the core of the earth, the central sun, a point in the upper atmosphere, etc.) Picture a vortex opening through you that connects deeply into the universe and feeds you energy. Be with that connection for a little while. Allow the merger fully. Breathe deeply.
- Reach for one of your power animals/animal guardians/spirit guides in the form of an animal. You are asking for them to appear (clairvoyantly not physically).
- Let the vision become what it will. This is not an exercise about mental control or demands on spirit. Allow the guide entry who appears, not who you demand to be seen. The situation may surprise you with a guide you had not considered before.
- Though your pace will stay constant, the vision may be to "run" or "fly" with them. Allow yourself to "shift" as a shaman/shape shifter does *within the vision*, if that is the relationship you have with your animal. Feel them merge with you. Allow their power and yours to become one.
- You may encounter more than one animal guide on your walk to merge and spend time with.

- Your visions could take you to other places, communications and times. Allow whatever comes to come. Remember that you are always in control and may ask that it stop at any time if you become overwhelmed by it.

This exercise will strengthen all of your personal communication gateways with spirit. Remember to care for your physical body by not getting lost in it and pushing too hard. There is a lot of energy that moves through you when you engage in this way, and you will need to take a shower/cleanse and rest to allow the building blocks to align when you are finished.

****

Astrology for Daily Use

Astrology studies the movements of the sun, moon and planets and their connection to everyone and everything on earth. It has been called *the first science* as it is known to have been used by the Mayans, Egyptians, Pythagoras, Nostradamus and Isaac Newton just to name a few. Daily horoscopes for-the-masses have attempted to narrow a very expansive course of analysis and study into a sentence or two in the newspaper daily, but in truth, this science can be used with much greater personal accuracy if used correctly.

Along the important line of creating a language of communication with Spirit and the Universe for decision-making, astrology offers a wonderful set of symbols, variables and flow that can be watched and "felt into" psychically once you learn the basics. You don't need to be able to create or even read charts to benefit from learning a bit of what is going on in the universe. To get started, we recommend the very fun and informative *Complete Idiot's Guide to Astrology*. This builds a wonderful basis to move into deeper study of astrology should you wish to, but at the very least gives you monthly and daily awareness of the energies available for use.

****** **Mastery Work Exercise** ******

Connecting thru Astrology & the Planets

There is a great deal of change going on in the universe and the earth is undergoing its own transition and ascension process. This is an amazing thing to plug into. Shamanism provides a lot of "of the earth and animals" connection, and a good way to balance this out is to tune into planetary energies. This can be done in a simple, fun way that also adds to your symbol database for guide/mediumship communication. We want you to be able to start closing your eyes, reach out and feel planetary alignments and changes. Sound like too big a task? It is amazingly simple. Here is how you do it:

We recommend you purchase the book: *The Complete Idiot's Guide to Astrology.* Each day you start your meditation by getting centered a bit and then reading the description of the attributes of one planet or one sign or one transit/link (conjunction, trine, opposition). You are not studying to be an astrologer who creates charts. You are allowing yourself to plug into the cosmos. After you read the planet and learn about it, close your eyes, drop back into meditation, reach out with your consciousness to that planet and introduce yourself. Allow yourself to be in its presence. Feel the elements you just learned about it and whatever else it wishes to share. This is a magical exercise.

And it's as simple as that to lay your foundation. Once you have done this…and it takes at least 29 days (12 signs, 12 planets, about 5 definitions of how planets can interact, one per day maximum)…I recommend you purchase an astrology calendar of some kind that provides the basic aspects for each day. This guide will tell you what sign the moon is in, when planets form important angles and connections to each other and the signs it is happening in. After you have learned the planets and signs for yourself, you can take this basic information such as "Mercury trine Saturn"…reach into that "situation" and get your own energetic "read" on what this will bring. You will find that this will increase your connection at a planetary level as well as broaden your mediumship/intuitive abilities. Human/society training has many conditioned to think a single course of study is a self-contained "island" for mastery that requires 20 years of practice to deserve access to. But this is not so. Remember that every exercise gives you direct access if done respectfully and will actually feed into the building blocks of your abilities at other levels as well.

****

Meditation...the key to it all

There are many misconceptions in the world today about the concept of meditation. Some believe it's an irrelevant practice or hobby for new age people. Others feel that since they can never seem to quiet their mind, or lead too busy a life that it's an option easily skipped. But we can tell you beyond a shadow of a doubt that this is the key to nearly every issue in a person's life.

Think that's too big of a statement...?

The true purpose of Meditation is really to train and discipline the mind to move into stillpoint, and the way to do this is to focus and practice. People can quite easily close their eyes, listen to music or a guided meditation and move into altered state. Others do this naturally when they walk, run or dance if a steady rhythm is focused on. The chatter of the mind naturally begins to quiet more and more even if you spend only 15 to 30 minutes a day doing this with intent. And from there, a cascade effect occurs. Health improvements are common, as illness begins first on the mental-emotional planes before grounding in the physical body as disease. Many people notice that in the face of everyday issues, confrontations and challenges; they realize they are beginning to *react* differently. Things that used to be irritating or upsetting, no longer feel like such an issue. Problem-solving and decision-making becomes clearer and more accurate, and sleep patterns get deeper. Indeed, much is changing on the inner and outer planes of existence. And for intuitives and mediums, meditation and altered-state are the realms of deeper communication. The Spirit Guides we work with often say:

"We are so honored to work with those who call on us and speak to us regularly...now if only more people would take the time to be still so that they could become aware of our messages and manifestations...to hear us answer."

Taking the time to be still and listen is the only path to mastery, and we encourage you not to believe those who tell you that it's very difficult and will take years before you can achieve deep, true meditation. This is not so. The universe reads and creates manifestations from intention. So each and every time you "sit" with the intention of quieting your mind, you will have achieved a step. And taking that step daily, without excuses, will increase you connection to your higher self's guidance so that everything in your world will have the opportunity to feel the positive effects.

Here are some tips & tools to assist you:
1. Sit in a comfortable chair so that your back is straight and supported, your feet firmly planted on the floor, your hands comfortably in your lap, palms up if possible (You receive energy through the chakra points in the hands.) You should not lay down, because this is a cue for relaxation to take you into a sleep-state, and that is not the same as meditation.
2. Be sure you select a time when you will not be interrupted. Turn off the phone and close the door to the room you are sitting in. This will assist the energy to build up in the room around you. Be very careful that no one and nothing will suddenly touch you or make a startling loud noise. You won't realize how deep you are, and for those of us who work as deeply as trance, we can tell you that there is a very real danger of being thrown into physical shock if touched during meditation.
3. Breathe gently and slowly in through your nose and out through your mouth. This may naturally change as the meditation progresses, and that is appropriate.

4. Don't cross your legs or arms, as this cuts off the energy flow (lotus position is the only exception). Focus on relaxing one part of your body at a time.
5. You may use music or a guided meditation CD to lead you if you find this helpful. It's good to give your mind something to focus on in the beginning.
6. Using custom selected aromatherapy essential oil blends in a diffuser can assist you in moving more quickly into altered state as well.
7. Light a candle and focus on the flame if you would like an occasional alternative to closing your eyes. Light is a powerful force in the universe including all of the colors of the rainbow and love in a living, breathing manifestation. You can feel free on a regular basis to have a candle lit in the room with you when you meditate. This ritual also sets up your power of intention.
8. 'Sit' in the same place at the same time each day if possible. There is no time on the spirit plane, but this sets up a sort-of 'appointment' with your Spirit Guides for them to assist and work with you. After you have done this for awhile, don't be surprised if you feel them 'pulling' on you when you miss a meditation appointment!

Energy, Manifestation & Universal Law

How do we know which way we should go…?
How does creation work…?

As decision-making is a requirement for creation and manifestation, Universal Law is the "rule book." A merging of intuition and intellect under the framework of these rules creates a provable, visible recipe for deliberate creation. Action-reaction. Science at its core. Life can be extremely frustrating when you don't know *why* you are attracting repetitive circumstances, or can't seem to accomplish your goals. These foundation laws outline how the universe functions across all planes of existence and brings clarity to be merged with other aspects such as timing and soul intent for a life. Often our quest for the higher spiritual and soul-level answers gets ignored in the pursuit of physical demands. We encourage you to add an understanding of Universal Law to your intellectual awareness, and then move beyond it to individual soul purpose through meditation and decision-making. Here are the materials we recommend for ongoing study:

❖ Esther and Jerry Hicks have been providing channeled information for more than 20 years and we find them to be of great assistance in simplifying and learning the basics of Universal Law. They channel a guide they call Abraham and you can choose any of their materials to work with from books to audio CD's.

❖ A second, more advanced guide to all of the Universal Laws can be found in Dr. Norma Milanovich's book entitled *The Light Shall Set You Free*. This book has fantastic charts that outline choices and behaviors and the direct effect they have on manifestation, as well as extensive information on those souls who have played a major role in humanity, and multi-dimensional definitions of the celestial hierarchies. This is an important guide to understanding the universe and charting a path to soul growth and personal transformation.

❖ As everything in the universe is made up of energy, the next important step we recommend is learning about the energy systems of the body and how creation and interaction works on a personal level. Identifying where and how blockages can occur as well as the effect of choices made can complete the circle of understanding. Caroline Myss is an amazing author, medical intuitive and lecturer who is able to truly bring this process to clarity through her *Energy Anatomy* series on CD/book set.

❖ Application of Kinesiology is another fantastic method of communicating with your higher self, your body and spirit. In his book *Power vs. Force*, David Hawkins applies the use of kinesiology with an understanding of the levels of energy inherent in everything from words to business applications. This is a must-read for applying energy use to practical daily interactions and decision-making.

****** **Direct Channeling from Spirit** ******

Manifestation & the Progression to Crisis
What is it do you think that brings crisis into your life experience...? Do you believe, truly, that it is an outside source...? Many Practitioners cling to three belief systems at once. Victimhood, which is a learned society behavior and allows for avoidance of self responsibility; the tenants of Universal Law and manifestation principles; and the hope-fear-anger elevations.

We are here to provide for you, but through truth and resources designed to strengthen you rather than do it for you. Yes, we assist once you have set your course through decision-making (conscious and subconscious), and intentions. This is how the universe works. Not through demands on the law of attraction that many have described as a magic wand that requires nothing more than a declaration...as if multiple layers of intention and soul growth are exempt from the process. We provide for you here a visual diagram for you to meditate upon. We encourage you to consider how your life and choices currently act upon the true wheel of manifestation. Through connection to your higher self in merger with this, many discussions can be had with your guides, and new realizations will be graced you if you choose to consider and study this.

So how do you arrive at what seems to be "crisis points" in your life experience then...? The simple answer is that you choose them. And rather than give you the standard metaphysical lecture about lessons and growth, we will get right to the solution point we know you want...how to get out of the crisis....or avoid its arrival altogether.

The soul, we will say for simplicity, has a list of accomplishments it wishes to achieve in the life. It also has set up opportunity to do so through implanting tools, resources, interactions and abilities at certain junctions in the life line of the incarnation. The soul whispers at first to the personality of the truth, and suggests a solution of action that must be taken to achieve soul growth. When the personality resists, the soul amplifies the discomfort in an attempt to push the personality through the falsehoods of illusion and fear. And finally, if the personality continues to halt the soul's progress and growth, it will commission an undeniable "crisis point" in the hopes of achieving the necessary transition.

Though each situation that occurs in a life must be analyzed for the truth of it and its origin, we provide here the main learning structure and invite you to consider that walking through new doors and dedicating yourself to listening and responding to the whispers might be more enjoyable and peaceful a life choice than waiting for illness, relationship explosions and physical situations that are much less pleasant.

And what of the earth changes and escalation of this cycle that the humans are now choosing to face...? They have disrespected the planet, each other and themselves. They have certainly ignored the whispers. What level of soul lesson do you think will be enacted at this point...? And more importantly, where will you find yourself in the transition...?

We will tell you that the key is your dedication to working directly with us every day now and interacting with us while you are NOT in crisis or dealing with issues that frighten or uncenter you. This will determine your ability to easily and instantly know how to react when you must.

Use kinesiology so much for unimportant things like asking your body which vitamins to take or food to eat at each meal. Use it at the grocery store to ask what you are out of and can't remember. Use your direct energy to "reach" into a book or movie you haven't yet seen to "feel" if you will enjoy it, and then watch it or read it to see if you were correct in your intuitional assessment. Use your internal guidance to "feel" the list of work projects on your desk and practice following knowingness, not intellect alone in deciding the best order to do them in, to allow heightened efficiency and the opportunity for your guides to build support around other projects that may be more challenging and are not to be taken on alone. ASK your team of guides and guardians for assistance with the projects you must attend to in your life and listen for answers and solutions to come in from any direction. (You are one half of the team conversation, so if you don't ask or discuss it with them, they will not interfere.) Practice standing still in your life and waiting for the heartbeat that tells you "now" is the time to move in action. And above all else, take responsibility for preparing the easier path by "sitting" with your guides in meditation each day. There need be no visions or plan or ability there. Just intention for release, reaching for the silence and peace, and to allow spirit to help strengthen you.

You do these things with the small, unemotional, non-crisis communications and decisions so that when a decision is necessary or situation occurs that frightens you, you will have built your trust in yourself and communication bridge with spirit strong enough so that you are able to stay centered, react with less fear and from a point of higher-self knowingness and mastery. Your guidance will feel and be more clear and certain to you. And you will know when to move.

This is the pathway of the true light worker and practitioner. You will no longer be supported in the old way of allowing crisis, acting surprised by it and then having the luxury of running to an outside "psychic" to solve it for you. Those days are fading away. You must now walk your mastery or miss your chance to walk into the new dawn being created. This is why so many of the primary teachers have been "pulled back." Commissioned by millions of souls for the chance to learn from them, they now know they must let you take responsibility for yourselves in using the available tools in dedication to yourselves. Many of you, in retrospect, know your truth, what needs to be changed, and what the very next step is to accomplish it when viewing any area of your life. Not for one minute have you ever been alone, nor has the solution (or problem) been a mystery.

The Manifestation Process

Manifestation is not just ask-and-the-law-of-attraction-brings-it as many teachings simplify it into being. We provide for you here a step-by-step outline and visual diagram of the elements that feed into the manifestation process. This is provided for you to meditate upon and consider any situation in your life and how it came into being.

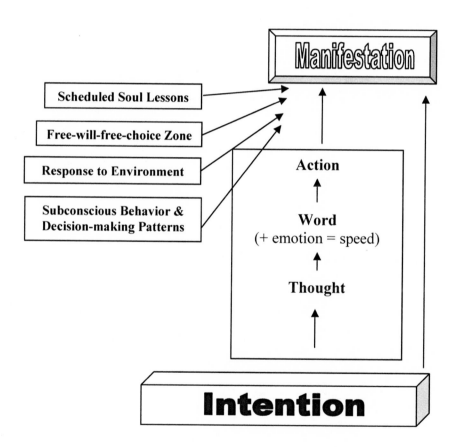

The 4 Primary Pathways of Manifestation…
1. Focused-Relaxation Manifestation – The Universal Law of Attraction in action
    *   The missing link → we always receive based on *intention* behind request not the demand of the thought/word/action
2. Scheduled / Soul Level Lessons
3. Free-Will-Free-Choice/Response to the Environment
4. Subconscious Pattern Manifestation (both positive & negative)
    *   Release by Realization those that are not positive and supportive
    *   If you can see it you can walk away from it and choose something different

Deliberate Creation occurs when you understand and practice…
1. Joy vs. Fear Decision-Making = realization of intention. Any decision made with fear as the *true* intention will have a negative result. You can't be dishonest with yourself about this because the results will prove the foundational intent.
2. Working with Spirit for in-the-moment merge using tools like kinesiology, mediumship, etc.

Manifestation Keys…
1. Balance (meditation, aura clearing, etc.)
2. Union with Silence = Union with Creation
3. Balance + Union = Detachment vs. Fear
4. Heightened Sensitivity on purpose allows flow with Divine Design, knowingness & guide communication

Aromatherapy

The actual application and use of essential oils to assist in healing dates back across many cultures before recorded history including use by the Egyptians, Greeks and Romans. The term "Amomatherapie" was invented by French scientist Rene-Maurice Gattefosse after he discovered that soaking his burned hand in lavender oil healed the wound completely with no sign of scarring. In the 17th century there was another advance in the field during the Black Plague in Europe, when practitioners who used and traded in lavender perfumes were found to be nearly immune. During World War II, Dr. Jean Valent used essential oils to successfully treat battle wounds and later worked with psychiatric patients and found he was able to wean them off of chemical medicines. Today, essential oils are used to address a variety of physical, mental and emotional concerns. In their pure state, on a physical level they have antibacterial, anti-fungal, anti-infectious, anti-inflammatory and antiseptic properties depending on the specific oil. In the purest essential oil state they are 50-100 times more potent than their herb form.

So how do they work…?

Our olfactory system (inhaling through the nose) is a direct link to the brain and central nervous system. The natural healing properties of the oil can initiate a direct and nearly immediate effect on mental and emotional issues. Some can stimulate concentration, alertness or physically energize. Others have properties that cause a calming effect and assist in releasing stress, fear, insomnia or trauma. Our bodies have the ability to use and process pure essential oils naturally, and at the molecular level. It is extremely important to use only aromatherapy products that are 100% pure vs. synthetic. Aromatherapy has become a trendy sales tool in large commercial products such as candles, soaps and other mass produced products. These synthetic-artificial products such as air fresheners have a larger molecular structure than pure oils and cause allergies and other issues as they are processed within the body as toxins. While pure products may be a bit more expensive, we encourage you to be wise in your application and purchasing to avoid artificial and often toxic products. The second important factor to consider is potency. Many commercial products, and even some of the more custom ones, save money by putting only one drop of true oil into their mixture so they can claim purity, but these consistencies are usually not strong enough to allow the healing properties to reach the central nervous system.

We recommend a fantastic reference book entitled *Aromatherapy for the Soul* by Valerie Ann Worwood, which provides a metaphysically-based guide to the healing properties and effects of more than 70 essential oils.

Working with Stones and Crystals

In Native American tradition, great reverence was paid to working with the spirits of both animals and 'the stone people.' Crystals are used as conduits in a variety of scientific applications today, and throughout recorded (and unrecorded) history we find references to crystals used in healing and more. As we seek to work in harmony to transform ourselves and humanity, there has never been a more important time to explore the energies and assistance that can be found in the wide variety of crystals and semi-precious stones now available.

Each stone or crystal, as with all objects and life forms in the universe carries a very specific vibration and consciousness. In and of themselves they should not be assigned the power, but instead, think of them as partners offering assistance. Their vibration, interacting with yours, can assist in shifting the energies when combined with the true seat of power, which are your intentions. The power is always within you, but assistance from the mineral kingdom is truly available to those who enjoy working with them. Selection can be done through pure intuition (if you are drawn to it and it feels good then this is an indication that it can be of assistance to you in some way), or, you may go in search of a particular type of stone to assist with a specific issue.

We recommend two excellent guides to explore with. *The Book of Stones* is a larger and incredibly comprehensive reference that goes into great depth regarding the origin and applications. *The Crystal Bible* is an easy-to-carry, more summarized option with excellent application and vibrational information. Both contain color photographs for easy identification.

Mediumship
All mediums are psychic…
but not all psychics are mediums.

Reading another person or situation *psychically* is done at a different, slightly lower frequency than working *mediumisticly*. It can be said that a medium literally plugs in to a higher vibration and is able to see spirit clairvoyantly or hear them clairaudiently. This ability can be compared to an oscilloscope that reads the level of electronic current not visible to the naked eye, or being able to hear a dog whistle.

So how does it work…?

One way to visually describe the interaction is by using a scale from one to twelve. Level one is conscious normal conversation and interaction on the physical plane with another person. In the same room, spirit is present but they are operating vibrationally at Level 12. A medium has the ability to move into altered state and shift their vibration to Level 6. Spirit 'dials it down' from Level 12 to Level 6 and merges with the medium *on the internal planes* to have a conversation. Trance mediums may move so deeply into altered state that they literally allow spirit to merge with their physical body so that they can use the medium's vocal cords to speak. This is NOT possession. It is a very protected and reverent process similar to tuning a radio to the right station. Platform mediumship, as is demonstrated by John Edwards on television, mixes mediumship with psychic linking to relay messages. A medium can build energy through movement and pacing that assists in accessing and maintaining the link.

Mediumship has become more popular and has wider acceptance since mass media production of the television show *Medium, Ghost Whisperer* and others. As it holds great fascination for people, it is also prone to misuse, ego and drama. While mediums might receive information and see spirit, which is amazing in and of itself, it's important to leave the drama of the movies out of the equation. Someone who is truly working with spirit vs. promoting their own ego will engage in the act with reverence and subtlety. Working with spirit is not a circus. Functioning mediums have spirit guides who protect them and act as gatekeepers who assist and help control interaction and energy flow. Classical British Mediumship focuses on interacting and communicating with those who have died in this lifetime. A more expansive view of the use of mediumistic abilities overlaps to include working directly with spirit guides. What is important for each individual is to begin through focused intent to use meditation and balancing tools to consciously start interacting with your own Guides to build a language, confidence and build in controls for working with your abilities. There is no need for drama. The earth plane is a free-will free-choice zone that allows you to build a framework of interaction that is comfortable for you. There is no need to be frightened or experience unwanted interactions and visions once you begin to work with these abilities with focused intent.

If you would like to learn more about mediumship, *The Beginner's Guide to Mediumship* is one of the few books devoted solely to mediumship that emphasizes the practical application of this ancient practice to modern life. And it's not just for beginners. Larry Dreller's intimacy with the art is apparent in his definition of the medium as separate from the psychic and channeler, as well as in his concern about the possible dangers inherent in this work. He wisely devotes nearly half the book to understanding the precautions that should be taken. Anyone with an interest in mediumship will get something from this book, not the least of which is an awareness of how our lives interact with the realm of the spirits.

Balancing, Clearing & the Aura

Being a Sensitive can actually be quite an extensive package of both abilities and challenges, and learning how to take care of ourselves at this level isn't something that our parents and teachers necessarily knew how to do. Empaths, those with the ability to remove or ease the pain of others actually do so naturally, and this can cause illness if the aura and body of the empath isn't consciously cleared regularly. Sensitives are like channels or conduits for information and energy to flow through, which also means that we must learn some simple techniques to clear ourselves.

For those of you who step forward and assist others we encourage you to get serious in the care of yourself by becoming more disciplined about daily meditation, and working with some focused chakra and aura clearing methods. The chakras are the energy centers of the body, and our aura consists of physical, mental, emotional, spiritual and etheric layers around our physical bodies. These energy centers and layers pick up, merge with, and touch the energy of others when we interact with them. Our own mental processes and emotional ups and downs can cause shifts and blockages as well.

There are more than a few things that can be difficult for a sensitive/intuitive that wouldn't bother a regular person, and learning the truth about yourself can bring great empowerment and self acceptance. Crowds can quickly bring sensory overload; fluorescent lights can feel like needles on the skin; touching or spending time with a negative, angry person can be the psychic equivalent to being physically hit; eating foods with preservatives in them can quickly cause physical illness or low-grade dis-ease. People don't realize that all physical objects carry the energy and memories of the things that occurred in their presence. This is why old houses with antiques can be very uncomfortable. Photographs of people can also cause discomfort, because looking at them can initiate an instantaneous connection and intuitive reading.

Yes, it's true that the more practiced you become at working with your own energy, the easier it can become to protect yourself and manage interactions. But for many of us, our sensitivities are so strong that it's only possible to process what we encounter and read, avoid certain situations and interactions, and then put in place practices to process the energy out of our systems. Here are a few recommendations to assist you...

Techniques for Energy Clearing & Balancing

This might sound too simple, but actually one of the best tools to clear your aura is to shift your schedule to taking a shower at the end of the day before going to sleep at night. This literally washes all the energy you picked up from others out of your aura and can bring immense relief. The dreamtime is a serious place, and can be just as busy for high-functioning intuitives as the waking hours. We leave our physical bodies behind and travel far inter-dimensionally and astrally, interacting with many energies along the way. Entering into this space with the energies picked up all day can lead to chaotic astral plane interactions and difficultly sleeping. This is then also a clearing process that should be done in reverse. Getting up in the morning and washing your hair will clear the lingering dreamtime energies picked up in other dimensions and while traversing the astral plane. Bedding should be changed and washed at least once per week, or more often depending on how sensitive you are. Using water is a natural cleansing tool, and we also strongly suggest you use 100% natural soap and body products that contain organic and/or essential oils. We recommend *ZUM soaps from Indigo Wild*. They are 100% natural, handmade and contain a very high percentage of therapeutic essential oils. Sea salt & Citrus is a favorite. The salt clears away negativity, and the citrus uplifts. We also recommend a fantastic CD set called *Chakra Balancing: Body, Mind and Soul*, by Deepak Chopra. It's helpful to use something like this or do a mindful personal practice equivalent at least once per week as a focused method to more deeply clear and align your energy centers. This particular set contains a wonderful healing music CD for meditation or sleeping at night, and then a second CD with guided meditation.

And finally, a balancing-your-energy-and-body discussion would not be complete without talking about how to nourish your physical body in a difficult world. Preservatives and processed foods have flooded the marketplace and our busy lives make it tough to spend hours preparing meals. We recommend, as much as your budget will allow, eating organic foods (without pesticides and chemicals added), and avoiding processed meals and preservatives. One method of getting a daily dose of good nutrients, vitamins and minerals into your body is by using a blender. Tossing an array of fruits and vegetables into a blender takes only minutes and can be a great snack or meal once a day. Using chocolate or vanilla almond or soy milk and fruit can literally hide the taste of the raw (and very healthy) vegetables you toss in like broccoli, brussel sprouts, beets and carrots! We love the book by Sandra Cabot entitled *Raw Juices Can Save Your Life*. It's fun, easy, gives you lots of recipe ideas, and seriously outlines all of the properties and choices for each possible ingredient so that you can pick and choose the ones that will support healing any physical ailments you might also be experiencing.

Himalayan Salt Lamps and Selenite

Salt is one of the great purifiers graced and available to us on this planet, and we highly recommend the use of Himalayan Salt lamps to harmonize the energies and release any negativity that can build up in the body, rooms at home and at the office. We also recommend Selenite in lamps and candle holders for its inter-dimensional properties and assistance for practitioners in entering and maintaining communication in altered states of consciousness.

Homeopathy

As we try to maintain good health and attend to wellness, we find homeopathy becoming more and more mainstream. This is a medical specialty that uses diluted natural substances known as 'remedies' to stimulate the body's built-in capacity for healing. Potency is achieved by both diluting and shaking these remedies in the preparation process. It is a fascinating science used across many cultures throughout the ages in a variety of forms, but the current method of use was discovered by Samuel Hahnemann more than 200 years ago. It is built on the proven principle that like cures like. In other words, any substance that causes a combination of symptoms in a healthy individual, can actually cure similar symptoms in the sick. Essentially, homeopathy offers a very diluted, safe way to use a poison to treat illness by following the symptoms. These remedies have proven enormously successful in providing highly effective cures for many illnesses without side effects, complications or contraindications to standard medications. And a single remedy can initiate a cascade of healing throughout the entire integrated being, improving a person's physical, emotional and mental well-being.

If you have an interest in learning more about homeopathy, we highly recommend Dr. Edward Shalts book entitled *Easy Homeopathy – the 7 Essential Remedies You Need for Common Illnesses and First Aid* and *The Illustrated Encyclopedia of Healing Remedies* by C. Norman Shealy, MD, PhD. Walking into the health food store and looking at the overwhelming array of alternative remedies can be frustrating. These books can bring great clarity in explaining how homeopathy works, how to work with a homeopath, and simple charts for diagnosis and remedy application for your self. Please be aware that we recommend consulting a medical doctor should you be in need of medical care, and it is not our intention to offer medical advice, simply a fascinating guide to assist you in exploring the many opportunities for good health and well-being that we have found to be successful.

Feng Shui

Feng shui is the art of placement, and can provide us with greater tranquility in our living environment as well as transformation assistance. In the strange and amazing inter-workings of the universe where everything is connected, people often don't realize the absolute correlation between their physical living environment and life circumstances. A true metaphysical practitioner can walk into a home and very quickly identify where a person is stuck in their life issues by the condition of the house, layout and presence of certain elements and objects.

There are a variety of schools of feng shui, but we encourage the application of *intuition* above any 'form school.' Too often students are taught a ridged dogma that insinuates that objects contain an absolute power in and of themselves, rather than properly assigning the power of transformation and manifestation to the individuals power of intention first, merged with application. All objects carry vibration and consciousness as well as memory, and can certainly be joined with the soul's intention, but following internal guidance and flow is the actual key to using feng shui to nurture your soul and life.

As you embark on working with feng shui for transformation, we would recommend you do so by using the elements, your intuition and the four directions. This will naturally bring you to the Compass Method of calculating the areas of your home if you would like to work with the traditional Bagua mapping. Always with the prime directive of following your soul, just remember that if it feels good, it's good feng shui. This initiates a higher form of application that can be guided beyond the basics. Two excellent books we recommend to merge both levels of application and have some fun include *Feng Shui for the Soul* by Denise Linn; and Lillian Too's *168 Ways to Energize Your Life*. Another reference book we truly enjoy that can be applied to both communication with spirit and nature, as well as applied to working with these energies in your home is *In the Shadow of the Shaman* by Amber Wolfe. This is a truly magical guide that links together much elemental and symbolic energy, and gives practitioners a great intuitional feel for their flow and application.

Further Exploration
Earth Change Updates & Ongoing Communication

Should you have an interest in additional subjects such as the role of the extra-terrestrial races, health alternatives and ongoing communications; you are invited to visit the website at **www.EternitysFire.com** where you can sign up to receive notices of earth change updates, channelings for practitioners, new mastery work exercises, and learn about additional direct resources. In this monumental time of transition, this website is provided as a portal for those practitioners who wish to stay connected.

9 780615 433820